THE WINNER EFFECT

THE WINNER EFFECT

How Power Affects Your Brain

Ian Robertson

B L O O M S B U R Y

LONDON · BERLIN · NEW YORK · SYDNEY

First published in Great Britain 2012

Copyright © 2012 by Ian Robertson

Bloomsbury Publishing Plc
50 Bedford Square
London WC1B 3DP

www.bloomsbury.com

Bloomsbury Publishing, London, New York and Berlin

A CIP catalogue record for this book is available from the British Library

Hardback ISBN 978 1 4088 2473 3
Trade Paperback ISBN 978 1 4088 3189 2

10 9 8 7 6 5 4 3 2 1

Typeset by Hewer Text UK Ltd, Edinburgh
Printed in Great Britain by Clays Ltd, St Ives plc.

MIX
Paper from
responsible sources
FSC® C018072

To Fiona and our wonderful children
Deirdre, Ruairi and Niall, with love and gratitude

Contents

Acknowledgements

This book would not have appeared without the creativity and encouragement of my agent Sally Holloway of Felicity Bryan Associates: she plucked the title from the text and helped me articulate what I wanted to say. Thanks so much also to Felicity Bryan for her immense help and judgement over many years and to Michele Topham and Jackie Head of Felicity Bryan Associates in Oxford. I am grateful also to Richard Pine of Inkwell Management in New York for his skill and enthusiasm in getting this book over the line. Peter Tallack was generous with his time in early discussions about the concept, so many thanks to him.

Bill Swainson of Bloomsbury has been unstinting in his encouragement and editorial skill; I am indebted to him, Nick Humphrey and his great team at Bloomsbury in London. I am also very grateful to Peter Joseph of St Martin's Press for assiduous and intelligent editing and his generous encouragement.

A number of my friends and colleagues have contributed their time in reading sections of this book. My Monday-night tennis partners indulged me with their helpful comments, just as they tolerate my abysmal tennis – thank you, Eamon O'Doherty, Tom Shipsey and Edwin Allen. Sincere thanks to Shane O'Mara,

Richard Piech, Redmond O'Connell, Josh Balsters, Jane Ohlmeyer and Dan Bradley of Trinity College Dublin, who gave very helpful feedback, and to Matthew Fuxjager of the University of Wisconsin. I also really appreciate the help of Bobby, Philip and Feichin McDonagh, and Bill Shipsey for their careful reading and perspective – thank you.

I am a cognitive neuroscientist, not a social psychologist, but this book has drawn heavily on the seminal publications of highly creative and remarkable social and cognitive psychologists. I would like to pay homage to the achievements of a number of these scientists, including: Dacher Keltner, Deborah Gruenfeld, Carol Dweck and Nathanael Fast of Stanford University, Adam Galinsky of Northwestern University, Joris Lammers of Tilburg University, John Bargh of Yale University, Oliver Schultheiss of the University of Erlangen, Roy Baumeister of Florida State University, Pamela Smith of the University of California at San Diego, Ana Guinote of University College London, Richard Nisbett and David Winter of the University of Michigan and many others. I apologise to the other fine scientists whose work I cite in this book for not mentioning them by name in these acknowledgements. I would also like to thank my colleagues at Trinity College Dublin for providing me with a wonderful academic environment in which to work.

Many thanks also to Geoffrey and Wendy Andrews and Steve O'Rahilly for their friendship, and we remember with affection and gratitude our dear Suzy Oakes, Steve's wife, who died on 31 July 2011.

My brother Jim is an inspiration of eternal youth – thanks for that, big bro.

Finally, to Fiona, my love and thanks for putting up with me for all these years and for teaching me so much about the mind. And to our dear and sparkling children Deirdre, Ruairi and Niall, you will recognise with a groan these words sung in perfect tune: . . . 'Don't stop, never give up . . .'

Ian Robertson, Dublin, September 2011

Foreword

The boss was in a rage. After the incident he ordered an email to be sent threatening disciplinary action if this happened again. A chief executive, after all, is paid to be tough: it's his job to make sure staff don't screw up. Especially when he heads up the biggest company in the world.[1]

How could this happen, particularly in his newly opened headquarters? The offices, each a breathtakingly glazed suite, were bathed in the soft green light of the nearby hills they overlooked so nobly. He had taken so much trouble with the architects – he even chose the silk wallpaper – to make sure that directors were insulated in these finest of aesthetically pleasing surroundings, inaccessible to other senior staff, yet still this sort of blunder could occur.

As high-performing executives they needed this isolation from the organisation in order to preserve the brilliance of the strategic leadership which had made this, in terms of assets, the world's biggest corporation. For people at his level, *everything* is important. It took pedigree to create this, and a boss of such quality needed things in his company to be just right. That's why, according to a book written by one of Goodwin's colleagues, he apparently threatened disciplinary action to the staff who allowed cheap pink wafers to be included among the morning coffee snacks in the directors' boardroom.[2] Hadn't he brought off the purchase of that huge Dutch company? These pink wafers could have been a disaster during the boardroom negotiations.

The boss didn't appreciate criticism – why should he when the company's share price had rocketed during his tenure? He insisted that his executives wear the same tie – one with the company's logo on it – and he was not at all happy when one senior financial analyst, James Eden, had the temerity to describe him as a 'megalomaniac'.[3]

It was not long after Sir Fred Goodwin's alleged rage over the pink wafers that his bank, the Royal Bank of Scotland (RBS), reported losses of around £24 billion, not far off US$50 billion. Soon after, his company was effectively nationalised by the UK government at a cost of £53.5 billion of taxpayers' money, over US$100 billion, and Sir Fred was out of a job.[4]

RBS was a very profitable bank until it recklessly over-reached itself by purchasing in 2007, despite the scepticism of financial journalists, part of the Dutch bank ABN Amro. It would very likely have survived the 2008 crash were it not for that decision, which was made around the same time that its chief executive, isolated from the rest of the company and from the world in his luxurious Edinburgh office suite, was preoccupied with wallpaper and pink wafers.

Ursula is one of three children from two different fathers, and as was the case for many children in her housing complex, neither father was around much for their upbringing. On 12 February 2011, the crumpled body of a stabbed forty-two-year-old woman was found in the elevator car of the Baruch Houses low-income project where Ursula lived.[5]

What caught the attention of *New York Times* reporter Michael Wilson a few days later when he was sent to 555 Roosevelt Drive, Lower Manhattan, was that the elevator car in which the body had been found was so clean: all the others were like graffiti-smeared, urine-stinking ashtrays.[6] Wilson ends the article on the murder with a comment from a former Baruch Houses tenant he met hurrying through the entrance hallway – the man only returned, as briefly as possible, to visit his father. 'I got the hell out of here,' the reporter quotes the ex-resident as saying.

In 2010, exactly thirty years after she first worked as a summer student intern at Xerox, Ursula was ranked by Forbes as the twentieth most powerful woman in the world.[7] The first black woman to become CEO of a Fortune 500 company, Ursula M. Burns heads up the Xerox Corporation. She had gained a place in the Polytechnic Institute of New York, and Xerox, through its graduate engineering programme for minorities,[8] paid for part of her graduate work at Columbia University, where she was awarded a master's degree in engineering.

Ursula's mother had scrimped and saved to send her to Cathedral High School, a Catholic, all-girls school on Manhattan's East 56th Street, an escape route from the poverty and stunted promise that pervaded the Baruch Houses. This education allowed her to enter the Columbia programme which included that crucial internship at Xerox.

After she graduated in 1981, Ursula began to work full-time for the company. It took just nine years before a senior executive, Wayland Hicks, offered her a position as his executive assist-ant. She was wary at first, fearing that this might be a dead-end helper role, but took the risk and accepted the job. By the following year, she had become executive assistant to chairman and CEO Paul Allaire and by 1999 she was vice-president for global manufacturing.

On 21 May 2009, Ursula M. Burns was named CEO to replace Anne Mulcahy, who was retiring. Not only was Burns the first black woman to lead a Fortune 500 company, but the transfer of the post was the first ever transfer of a Fortune 500 CEO role from one woman to another.[9]

These two stories throw up questions that this book sets out to answer. What makes a winner? Are people like Fred Goodwin born to success, or is it a result of chance and circumstance? Would Ursula M. Burns have been so successful if she hadn't been given the power of early management positions that kindled abilities that might otherwise not have been realised?

Why do some people have an enormous drive to win, while others shy away from success and power? What does power do to people – and what about powerlessness? Do success and power make you live longer and better – and if so, why? Is power really an aphrodisiac and if it is, how and why does it have this effect?

The question of winning underpins almost every part of our lives. Who wins is the factor that shapes our lives more completely than anything else. Winning is a drive as powerful as sex, and we all want to win, whether we are aware of it or not. Think of the ambitions swirling around the desks of any office; consider the emotions and skirmishes surrounding promotion and advancement. In its more naked form, look at the parents howling at the sidelines of the football pitch for the victory of their seven-year-old darlings. What are they shouting for? Winning. And they want it very, very badly. Why do we want to win so badly, and *what makes a winner*?

That is the question that I aim to answer in this book. In the first chapter, The Mystery of Picasso's Son, I consider the question of whether people are born into winning. This is not an abstract question – it is something that everyone should consider in relation to their beliefs about their own lives and, even more importantly, those of their children. This is because believing that you are born into success – that you are endowed with winner's qualities as opposed to *earning* your success – can leave some people demoralised and psychologically crippled. Whether you are a winner or not, in other words, can depend on your beliefs about winning and these preconceptions can, through biasing of the very firing of your brain cells, act as self-fulfilling prophecies.

I will challenge you to examine your own preconceptions about what lies behind your own achievements – or lack of them – and gauge what your own drive to succeed is. I will also encourage you to explore how you react to success and, more importantly, to failure, along the way explaining how your brain mediates these key aspects of your psychological make-up.

Chapter 2 offers another mystery – that of the changeling fish – and asks the follow-up to the question of whether we are born to win: *is winning a matter of chance and circumstance?* Ursula M. Burns is at great pains to reject any notions that her achievements at Xerox have anything to do with her gender or background, but would her success been quite so brilliant had she not been given the opportunities of an enlightened employer? Did the positions of status and power she was given by Xerox actually create – or at least kindle – the qualities and abilities that led her to becoming the twentieth most powerful woman in the world?

These are the questions that are raised in Chapter 2 and in answering them I will visit the boxing rings of Las Vegas, combat between California mice, and the lower rooms of the Olympic Games. I will show how indeed the chances of winning are shaped by many things, from home advantage to bodily posture. The winner inside can be raised up or crushed by subtle unconsciously mediated effects related to gender, race and age that we are completely unaware of.

Chapter 3 offers a third riddle – that of Bill Clinton's friend
Tony Blair and the question posed here is – *what does power do
to us*? As one of the most powerful men in the world, Sir Fred
Goodwin showed a pattern of behaviour towards his staff that
would be unusual in the vast majority of men of less elevated
status and power. Are the two things connected? Does power
change our personalities and patterns of behaviour? Can power
tip some people – Fred Goodwin, for instance – over some
notional peak into negative behavioural territory? And if so,
is this the modern manifestation of the notion that 'power
corrupts': how precisely does this happen?

Most of us have had bosses who have not handled power well
– you can probably think of an example of a previous or current
boss of yours. And if you are a boss, or a parent, or a teacher, or
a police officer, or a prison guard, or an older brother or sister,
how have you handled the power that flows from that role? Has
it changed you in some way, either negatively or positively? You
probably don't know the answer to that question yet. You won't
be an accurate assessor of your own ability to handle power and
your need for it, but, rest assured, your younger siblings, children, underlings, pupils, students or prisoners will be all too
aware of it, for better or for worse. After reading this chapter,
you will probably have a slightly better idea of what your own
need for power is.

In Chapter 4, The Mystery of the Oscars, I address the question of *why* we want to win so badly – what is the attraction of
power? Answering this takes us into a detailed consideration of
the self and its vulnerabilities, and of stress and how we differ in
our susceptibility to it. We will have to consider key aspects of
our own outlook which shape our resilience – and ultimately the
likely length of our own lives.

Chapter 5 asks whether winning has a downside. Does the

power that comes from success 'go to the head' of some people, leading to strange and at times harmful behaviour? Is power, as Henry Kissinger maintained, really an aphrodisiac, and if so, why is there such a link between sex and power?

And do men and women respond differently to power? Is it a coincidence that almost all of the world's worst dictators have been men, or is this simply a by-product of the fact that few women have gained such political power? How do power and morality intersect? Does power ennoble or corrupt, morally speaking?

In Chapter 6 we get up close and personal with power, addressing the question of what makes a winner at its most raw and intimate level. Almost everyone has had some power in their life – all human relationships have some element of power struggle about them. In relationships where there is an imbalance of power, for instance parent and child or older versus younger sibling, does simply being in the more powerful role distort some people's behaviour? Is the beastly older sister, say, who is so nice to her friends, obeying simple laws of power more than she is displaying hypocrisy? Why can human beings display such apparently inconsistent and contradictory behaviour, and how do their brains deal with these contradictions? Is there anything comprehensible about such wanton cruelty whether in a marriage or a political system?

The questions of success and power are so personal and so important in every aspect of our lives that we can get glimpses of their operation in our own minds. From time to time in the book, therefore, I will ask you to complete some exercises and questionnaires which will illustrate these often unconscious mental processes at work.

The answers to the questions of what makes a winner and how power affects us are as important to the life of every person as they are to the collective future of the human race. This is not just an ethical or theoretical issue, but a very physical product of the interplay between our self and its environment. By learning to be aware of these physical roots of power and success, we can better learn to control how power affects us and those around us.

The Mystery of Picasso's Son

Are we born to win?

Holding hands with their father, a six-year-old girl and her eight-year-old brother arrive at the mansion's gates. They ring the bell and wait, smelling the eucalyptus scent released by the rain that is falling steadily. It takes a long time before the concierge appears, peering out and demanding if they have an appointment. Their father stammers that they have.

'I'll see if the Master will receive you,' the old man says. They wait and wait.

'You'd better wait in the car,' the father mutters, but they stay. The concierge appears again, looking slightly shamefaced.

'The Master can't see you today. He's working.'

They trudge back to the car in silent humiliation. Again and again over the years they repeat this journey. Sometimes the Master sees them and sometimes he doesn't.

But on the next weekend he is available. Their father shoos the girl and boy into their grandfather's living room, urging them forward to embrace shyly the bright-eyed old man. A slight awkwardness soon passes and the children forget themselves, cautiously pleased as their grandpa folds animals and birds out of paper for them. Their father relaxes into the family moment too, absent-mindedly taking out a file to smooth a cracked fingernail. Suddenly the older man jumps up, snapping, 'It's ridiculous to use a nail file. Do what I do: file them against a corner of a wall.'

And from that moment on and for the rest of his life, the thirty-something Paulo Picasso did exactly that, just as he had adopted many of his father Pablo Picasso's other habits – eating fish with his hands was another such idiosyncrasy. As she was to recall in her 2001 memoir, *Picasso: My Grandfather*, watching these and countless similar interactions between the two made Paulo's little daughter Marina 'sick with shame'.[1]

Paulo – the frightened-looking, dressed-up three-year-old in his father's famous 1924 painting *Paul as Harlequin* – led a feckless life of drifting and heavy drinking. He could never hold down a job or even forge a life independent of his domineering, neglectful father. Paulo could not provide for his family, and his two children grew up supervised by social workers; his son Pablito would kill himself when he was twenty-four by drinking bleach two days after Pablo Picasso's funeral in 1973.

Paulo Picasso never seemed able to escape the shadow of his father, graduating from weekly supplicant – beggar almost – to part-time driver, and eventually, once his own family finally disintegrated, to live-in secretary and chauffeur to a father who never bothered to conceal his contempt for his son's lack of direction. Marina Picasso remembers one visit when Pablo Picasso took his son into a neighbouring room; she and her brother listened as their grandfather shouted, 'You're incapable of looking after your children! You are incapable of making a living! You're mediocre and will always be mediocre. You are wasting my time. I am El Rey, the King. And you – you are my thing!'[2]

Paulo did indeed become his 'thing' – but not for long. He died at the age of fifty-four, on 5 June 1975, just two years after his father died, after protracted family legal battles which left him an inheritance of five-sixteenths of Pablo Picasso's enormous fortune. Paulo's sad life could not have been in greater contrast with that of his famous father.

Does this story represent a more general point about the children of successful parents?

Here, then, is the question for this chapter: why was the success of Pablo Picasso, one of the most renowned artists in the world, so completely absent in the life of his son?

Take a moment to consider your own success, or lack of it, in your life so far. What do you believe is the reason for that? If you are in a position of power or powerlessness, to what do you attribute your current status? These are questions which Paulo Picasso very likely asked himself, as do most of us from time to time. But as you will see in this chapter, how we answer these questions in our own minds has fundamental effects on whether or not we become winners.

A very commonly held response to the above questions is that we are in some way born to win or to lose. This is the common-sense notion that becoming a winner – whether political, artistic, business or in any other domain – is a matter of breeding. For thousands of years the odds of success have indeed been stacked in favour of the privileged few by genes and well-arranged marriages, a production line for high-performing humans modelled on the racehorse stud and European royalty. In fact, whether they like it or not, a few billion of the earth's population still live by this notion and regard those of us who don't as loopy. This book will challenge their assumptions.

While such an idea might seem dated in first world countries with their egalitarian ethos, we still put a huge premium – consciously or unconsciously – on the 'bred' factors of height, gender and race. As a 2005 survey of Fortune 500 companies has shown, we still make our powerful CEOs overwhelmingly tall, male and white.[3] And as another piece of research indicates, IQ is a particularly important consideration for the selection of executives, with the strong underlying assumption being made by many that intelligence, ability and genius are bred, not earned. Yet here is the puzzle: if winning has so much to do with breeding, why do so many people who were born with so many advantageous genes – Paulo Picasso included – fall by the wayside in the race to lead a successful, or even happy, life?

Or was Paulo's failure an anomaly? Research by Morten Bennedsen and his colleagues at the University of Copenhagen in 2007 indicates that it was not. Bennedsen looked at businesses founded by entrepreneurs successful enough to have achieved limited company status. What happened when the founder of the business handed over control to a son or daughter, compared with when the chief executive was appointed from outside the family, he asked?[4]

If people are born to win, then the children of winners should also be more successful than others. Not necessarily so. Bennedsen scrutinised the handovers to new CEOs in over 5,000 companies and what he found was dramatic: where the succession was to a family member rather than an outsider, the profitability of the company dropped by at least 4 per cent around the time of the succession – and plunged even more for bigger firms in high-growth industries.

Being born to successful parents does not guarantee success. But business and art are quite different worlds and Pablo Picasso was clearly not a typical parent, so is there really anything in common between Paulo Picasso and the heirs of family businesses? There is, and the link lies in the psychology of success.

*   *   *

In 1996 Suniya Luthar of the Teachers College of Columbia University and Karen D'Avanzo of Yale University studied two groups of fifteen- to sixteen-year-olds in two very different high schools in the north-east of the United States.[5] One school was in a poor inner-city area, with a very low average income, 13 per cent of pupils were white and one in five families received food stamps. The other was a wealthy suburban school with one of the highest average incomes in the country, where 82 per cent of the pupils were white and virtually none received food stamps. Yet the researchers discovered that the richer adolescents were much more anxious and depressed, and used more cigarettes, alcohol, marijuana and other illegal drugs than their more economically impoverished peers (a discovery that has been replicated in other studies inside and outside the USA[6]). How can this be? Can we find a clue to Paulo Picasso's lack of success in this study?

On the face of it, Pablo Picasso's wealth, fame and extraordinary talent were so far removed from the bankers and lawyers in a US suburb that it may seem absurd even to consider comparing their families. And whatever happened to Paulo Picasso was not down to his having too much money. He survived as an adult on whimsically administered dole-outs from his father, who was his casual employer for most of his life, and these left him and his family poor until near the end of his life. But Paulo lived in the shadow of his father's extreme wealth, fame and genius – and as I will show later in the chapter, such shadows can become grimly tangible influences on the lives on whom they fall.

Suniya Luthar probed her data in subsequent studies[7] to find out why children of rich, successful parents might be unhappier than poorer pupils. She came up with a conclusion which resonated with an observation made about the economics of success by the economist Staffan Linder.[8] Linder observed that successful people's time is valuable and the higher their earnings the more each hour is worth. The economic logic for financially successful parents, then, is to maximise the family income by working long hours and contract out mundane household and childcare activities to lower-paid employees and services. This aligned with Luthar's observation: the rich, born-to-win children spent more time either on their own or with adults other than their parents than the poorer children and they therefore also felt less emotionally close to their parents. Paulo Picasso found it hard enough to get an appointment to see his father, let alone spend 'quality time' with him.

Michael Kimmelman interviewed Picasso's former wife Françoise Gilot and his three surviving children for the *New York Times* in 1996 at the time of the opening of a major Picasso exhibition at the Museum of Modern Art in New York. He wrote on the basis of these conversations: 'Picasso, tellingly, didn't depict his children when they were adolescents or young adults. Adoring toddlers were one thing, teenagers another, and in his art, as in his life, he lavished attention on the former but had not much time for the latter.'[9] But older children are as needful of parental attention as toddlers, and Paulo Picasso had to wait in the rain for it – leaving him distanced from his father in much the same way as many of Luthar's children of the wealthy were emotionally estranged from theirs.

It is not, Luthar argues, that the well-off parents in her study were being selfish or deliberately neglectful. On the contrary, if you asked them *why* they were working so hard and for such long hours, most would say it was for their children. After all, with the parents having achieved so much themselves, how could they wish for less for their offspring?

But Pablo Picasso was not an overworking, driven Manhattan lawyer. He was a neglectful father, narcissistically preoccupied with his own genius, who bequeathed a legacy of misery and suicides across the wreckage of his many families. Luthar's research did not throw up such yawning gaps between the success of suburban parents and their children as were apparent between Pablo and Paulo. Something else must have come into play.

The severed ear

In 1606 the famous painter Michelangelo Merisi da Caravaggio went on the run from a death sentence in Rome. The fact that he was renowned and had wealthy patrons could not protect him. Trouble followed him during his long flight from Naples to Malta to Sicily and then back again to Naples. Then, one night as he came out of his favourite and famously seedy bar-cum-brothel close to the port – the Osteria del Cerriglio – he was set upon by a group of men who hacked at his face with their swords.[10]

The attack was so savage that news was sent to Rome of his death – Caravaggio was as famous as he was notorious in his lifetime. Nor was the attack a random one – there was logic and symbolism to the violence of Italy in that era, and Caravaggio's facial disfigurement was known as a *sfregio*. This attack on the face symbolised revenge for an insult to the honour and reputation inflicted on the person who had ordered the attack – retaliation for symbolic 'loss of face' by real facial butchery. The art historian Andrew Graham-Dixon suggests that this person was Giovanni Roero, Conte della Vezza, whom Caravaggio had sufficiently insulted while in Malta to warrant this savage retaliation in the back streets of Naples.[11]

Caravaggio never recovered his health and strength after the attack. He left Naples by boat, believing himself pardoned for a murder committed on a Rome tennis court. But when his boat arrived at the tiny harbour of Palo, on the coast near Rome, he was thrown into Palo's fortress. Whether the fortress's captain was ignorant of the recent pardon, or whether Caravaggio's scarred face led to his being mistaken for another fugitive knight reputedly on the papal wanted list at that time, no one knows.

No matter the reason for his arrest, Caravaggio was seized and locked up in the bleak castle whose squat grey ramparts still bulge over the Tyrrhenian Sea thirty miles north-west of Rome. By the time one of the most famous painters of his era had talked or bought his way out of the dungeon, the boat on which he had arrived had left, carrying away a roll of his last paintings.

Caravaggio was desperate. Four years earlier he had fled Rome and in Malta was knighted in return for painting the *Beheading of St John* for the Cathedral in Valletta, where it still hangs. Scarcely knighted, he was ceremonially defrocked, probably for brawling. As his doomed circular journey from Rome to Rome via Malta, Naples and Sicily progressed, his paintings becoming ever more bleak and his imbroglios ever more convoluted.

But he still had friends in high places and once the news of his demise had been corrected, a pardon of sorts arrived from Rome, with the promise that he could return to his adopted city unhindered. Cardinal Scipione Borghese, who was then busy accumulating the art collection that today fills Rome's Borghese Gallery, had wangled the forgiveness – but for a price: a roll of Caravaggio's paintings for his collection. Without the pictures, the painter's safe return to Rome and escape from the gallows was not assured.

Now he was on his way back. Somehow or other the desperate artist, sick and weak from his injuries, managed to traverse the sixty miles of bandit-infested malarial swamp which lay between

Palo and the boat's final destination before returning to Naples, Porto Ercole, where he hoped to catch up with the felucca and his paintings. But the boat had already sailed for Naples when he reached Porto Ercole. He collapsed on the beach there, was carried to a hospice by monks and died on 18 July 1610. Hearing the news of the painter's death, Scipione Borghese anxiously tried to retrieve his booty, which by then had been returned to Naples in the felucca. In the end he only managed to lay his hands on a single painting – one of St John the Baptist – which hangs in Villa Borghese in Rome to this day.

If only the captain of Palo's fortress had not been so zealous, what bleakly wonderful pictures that scarred thirty-nine-year-old genius might still have painted. But what does the story of Caravaggio's tumultuous life have to do with whether or not people are born to succeed?

On 11 November 1973, a receptionist at the Rome newspaper *Il Messagero* picked up an envelope that bulged strangely. Curious, she opened it to find a crudely typed and misspelled ransom letter, a lock of long brown hair and . . . a severed ear.[12] Postmarked Naples 22 October, it had taken three weeks to arrive; the sender clearly had not had recent experience with Italian 'express' post.

John Paul Getty III's mother Gail Harris identified the hair as belonging to her seventeen-year-old son but she could not be sure of the provenance of the now decomposed ear, which had been neatly removed from its head with a razor blade or scalpel. She had already received ransom demands for $17 million, but until the arrival of the bulging envelope the police and press had assumed that Getty was party to his own faked kidnapping. Known as 'the golden hippie' by the Italian press, he had dropped out of school and sold jewellery in Piazza Navona in central Rome, taken part in left-wing demonstrations and poured obloquy on the greed of his wealthy family.

Once forensics established that the ear had been removed from a living body rather than a corpse, the urgency grew. The boy's father, Paul Getty Jr, who could barely pay alimony to his estranged wife Gail, let alone find a $17-million ransom, had received little of his billionaire father John Paul Getty's fortune because of his own weakness for the hedonist delights of the 1960s.

Grandfather J. Paul Getty had already refused to pay the ransom, saying that he had fourteen other grandchildren, and even after the ear was sliced off, it took the entreaties of his daughter-in-law to extract from him part of the reduced $3-million ransom – the remaining portion being lent to the boy's father at 4 per cent interest. John Paul Getty III was finally released after the reduced ransom was paid five months after his kidnap. A truck driver noticed him on the *autostrada* south of Naples, standing shivering and traumatised in a rain storm, his long brown hair hanging damply over the bloodied rump of gristle that was all that remained of his ear.[13]

John Paul Getty III's son Balthazar Getty didn't particularly like his suite, the best in the hotel, the luxuriously appointed nineteen-room La Posta Vecchia overlooking the Mediterranean Sea. But if it was good enough for Naomi Campbell and Sean Connery, then maybe he – an actor whose sum success to date was to play a gas-station attendant in *Natural Born Killers* and bit parts in a number of TV shows such as *Hawaii-Five-O* – should hang out there too, fashion model wife and new baby in tow.

The hotel had been built in 1640 as a seaside retreat for the Orsini family, who in 1693 had sold it to the Odeschalchi family. They had held on to it until 1960, when J. Paul Getty Snr, Balthazar's great-grandfather, had bought it for $566,000 from Prince Ladislao Odeschalchi, and spent a fraction of his vast fortune restoring it to grandeur and luxury.

During its rebuilding, basement ruins were discovered of a Roman villa which archaeologists concluded could well have been the remains of a home of Julius Caesar. This news suited its purchaser John Paul Getty Snr, who remarked, 'I feel no qualms or reticence about likening Getty Oil Company to an empire, and myself to a Caesar.'[14] The discovery fitted in nicely with his world view: he told friends that he believed he was the reincarnation of a roman emperor.

But it was enough for J. Paul Getty Snr that his spiritual and proprietorial linkage to Julius Caesar had been established: he only ever spent seventeen nights at La Posta Vecchia. The paranoid magnate had iron bars installed across the sea-view windows and reputedly spent each Mediterranean night locked in his bedroom with a loaded shotgun by his side.

Across the boundary wall of La Posta Vecchia loomed another building, of the history of which, it is reasonable to assume, Balthazar Getty would have been unaware, as he would not seem to be a man inclined to read ('Anything I want to know, I just ask,' he said when he was asked if had read the many books on the Getty dynasty.)[15] The building that cast its shadow over the hotel's swimming pool and lush garden was the very fortress of Palo in which Caravaggio's fatal last imprisonment had taken place and which the Odeschalchi family had kept when it sold La Posta Vecchia to Balthazar's great-grandfather in 1960. It cast an eerie atmosphere of doom and transient luxury over the lush gardens of the hotel.

Each of the three most recent generations of Gettys – Balthazar, his kidnappee father John Paul and his sixties hedonist grandfather J. Paul Jr – had been heroin users.[16] On 5 February 2011, Balthazar's father John Paul died aged fifty-three at his home near London, after a long period of partial paralysis and near-blindness caused by a stroke brought on by his earlier drug abuse.[17] The phenomenon of mixed-up, drug-using children of rich and successful people would not have surprised Suniya Luthar, who had observed the restlessly anxious moodiness and taste for mind-altering substances among the offspring of busy and distant parents. Whether Balthazar's dislike of his luxury suite in La Posta Vecchia was a symptom of a similar rich-kid restlessness or whether the Getty spirits or those of Caesar and Caravaggio were disturbing him, who knows?

The lives of Caravaggio and the Gettys intertwine around the grim sea fortress of Palo. Caravaggio's fame and success – artistic if not financial, because of his reckless lifestyle – flourished without the burden that a successful parent can impose on a child: in contrast to the family wealth and success of the Getty children and Paulo Picasso, he was born into a modest family which was plunged into poverty when the plague killed his grandfather and father in one night in October 1577. Was Caravaggio lucky that his father was not a great lord or a famous artist? Were Paulo Picasso and the Getty descendants cursed by the success and wealth of their parents?

If this is true, then we are faced with another puzzle: what *is* it about successful parents that sometimes deprives their children of the fruits of success? Does the psychology of success pass along through generations, and can it help explain the mystery of Picasso's son? It does, and it can, but to understand it fully, we have to consider one of the most important aspects of our motivation and personality.

Read through these questions and answer honestly how much they apply to you:

1. Do you prioritise getting ahead more than having a comfortable life?
2. In work, does the thought of performing about the same as others bother you?
3. If you feel like you are wasting time, does this make you feel restless and uneasy?
4. Do you always try to be the best at what you do?
5. Would you choose to work with a difficult but talented co-worker over a pleasant but less competent one?
6. Are you ambitious?
7. Does the thought of 'taking life as it comes' make you uneasy?
8. Do you plan ahead in your career?
9. Would you strongly resent being described as 'lazy'?
10. Do you feel at all 'driven'?

How many questions did you answer 'yes' to? The higher the number, the greater your level of *achievement motivation* is likely to be. These questions are similar to ones used in a bigger questionnaire called the Ray-Lynn AO scale devised by the Australian psychologist J. J. Ray.[18]

If you answered yes to many of these questions, you will recognise what I mean when I say that the motivation to achieve can feel almost like something physical impelling you. But does this feeling have any basis, outside of a fertile imagination? The answer is: yes, it does.

Kei Mizuno and colleagues at the Osaka City University in Japan wanted to see whether they could *see* achievement motivation at work in the brain.[19] Student volunteers first filled out an academic achievement questionnaire similar to the one above. Then Mizuno and his co-researchers gave all of them a difficult learning task to do while their brain activity was measured using a method called fMRI (functional magnetic resonance imaging).

Crucially, though, they told two randomly selected groups that they would be rewarded for their efforts in two different ways. The first group were told to do as well as they could, and that the better they did, the more money they would earn – up to a maximum of US $75. The second group, who were given an identical task, received no money at all but critically they were told that the task was an intelligence test: their only reward was a display of their performance on a feedback chart on which the higher their performance, the greater the number of squares that turned blue.

The results were remarkable. In the money-reward group, the students' level of achievement motivation on the questionnaire was not linked to the activity in a key motivational part of the brain called the putamen, which is located deep in the middle of the brain, within a structure called the striatum, and is a key part of a *reward network* which I will explain in a moment. But for the group to whom the task was described as an IQ test, the achievement motivation kicked in: even though there were no tangible rewards other than the blue squares, a striking relationship between putamen activity and achievement motivation emerged. The more academically driven the participants, the more this key brain centre for motivation and reward 'switched on' – but *only* when they thought their intelligence was being tested, *not* when they were simply doing it for the money.

That sense in people with a high need to achieve of being almost physically impelled to succeed is not an illusion, then: the more driven by ambition we are, the greater the level of neural activity that will be fired up deep in the brain. And the critical aspect of this drive is that it comes from inside, from intrinsic motivation; it is not triggered *only* by external incentives.

We are of course all motivated by a mix of internal and external motivation; the most common external motivator is money, but we also work for the approval of others or out of fear. Good managers know that keeping their staff motivated requires a judicious combination of internal and external spurs but the best managers discover how to flick the secret switch of intrinsic motivation in the brains of their key staff. Once this switch is activated, high achievement motivation people, like the IQ-motivated Japanese students – will put body and soul into their work with little thought for how much they are being paid for it. The challenge for bosses here is not to sabotage that internal drive by how they externally reward their underlings. I will explain how this can happen later in the book.

Achievement motivation, then, is a crucial ingredient for success in life, and part of the recipe for what makes a winner.

We do not know what Paulo Picasso's level of achievement motivation was. Clearly his drive to be a winner was not undercut by early wealth, so perhaps his heavy drinking was a response to a thwarted need to achieve. Academic achievement motivation is boosted by academic reward – good grades and praise from teachers, for instance – which builds a sense of competence and achievement,[20] and the equivalent is almost certainly true in other domains of life where many of us work as much for the satisfaction of a job well done, or for the respect and approval of colleagues, as we do for the salary. Perhaps Paulo Picasso never received a reward for his achievements, however modest, and so any nascent ambition was snuffed out.

Outside of the fMRI scanner, in real life, however, things are not quite as simply divided between external and internal. Although, as I just mentioned, it is important for bosses, teachers and parents to distinguish between external and internal rewards,

in reality we can never completely disentangle extrinsic rewards
like money from intrinsic ones like job satisfaction. Almost always
there will be a mix of motivations. Even in industries where financial bonuses dominate, such as investment banking and other
financial services, the money rewards are seldom entirely extrinsic.
They are also crucial tokens of status and success, signs of one's
competence, and hence burrow deep into the achievement motivation networks in ambitious people's brains.

We know this because of our knowledge about how a part
of the brain called the reward network operates. The key job
of this network is to make us feel good when we do things that
will help us and our genes survive – the most important being
eating, drinking and having sex. The central fuel of this system
is a chemical messenger called dopamine: the pleasure you get
after eating a slice of cheesecake, drinking a glass of iced water
on a scorching day or sinking back after an orgasm all arises
from dopamine being released in the reward network.

But most of us are rewarded by other things as well: the
sight of a teacher's gold star on a five-year-old's copybook
will also trigger a surge of dopamine in the reward network,
as will reading a glowing appraisal of your performance by a
line manager at work. Animals with stimulators implanted in
their reward network will keep pressing a lever which triggers
rushes of dopamine-induced pleasure, to the extent that they
neglect food and starve themselves. It was this reward network
in the Japanese students that Kei Mizuno investigated with the
supposed IQ-linked exercise in the fMRI.

Returning to the question of bonus-driven financial services,
we cannot assume that all that motivates and matters to the bankers and traders is the absolute size of these external rewards. We
know this because Klaus Fliessbach and his colleagues from the
University of Bonn in Germany showed that the reward network

is triggered not only by what rewards you yourself are receiving, but, crucially, also by what other people like you are getting, as was demonstrated by a study which I will come back to in Chapter 5.[21]

It follows that if the money-motivated group of Mizuno's students had been able to see fellow students earning more than them, then the money could have been turned from a purely extrinsic reward to a mixed extrinsic-intrinsic one. That would be a more accurate reflection of real life: yes, we want to earn as much as possible, but most of all, we want to do better than our neighbours. And we definitely don't want to do worse than them. This explains why many billionaires, rich beyond reason, still work feverishly to accumulate even more billions: it is no longer the extrinsic reward value of the money that motivates them – it is the need to achieve (and usually it is also a need for power, but that is for the next chapter).

Achievement motivation, then, is certainly not just about academic achievement, nor is it manifested only in the brain. Most working people, whether they are teachers, farmers, secretaries, accountants, actors or electricians, are on a twin track of seeking both extrinsic and intrinsic reward. John Miner of the State University of New York at Buffalo and colleagues showed this in a study of high-tech industries, finding that the motivation to achieve in the directors of young companies is a strong predictor of success, forecasting both growth in profits and increases in the number of people each company employs.[22]

And, on the other side of the world, J. J. Ray of the University of New South Wales with Satvir Singh of the Guru Nanak Dev University in India studied 200 Punjabi farmers and found that a small farmer's level of achievement motivation predicted how productive his farm would be over the next five years.[23]

Intrinsic motivation – wanting to do something for the sense of competence and achievement it gives – as opposed to purely extrinsic reward such as money, seems to burrow into our deepest ambitions. Equally, knowing that you will inherit billions of dollars can sabotage the development of such intrinsic motivation. Why is this the case?

Very few things we do are intrinsically motivating at first – except maybe such basics as sex and eating. So we learn motivation as children by doing something, such as playing a musical instrument and by gaining a sense of competence and achievement as we gradually get better at it. But most children have to be externally induced to get through the early stages until the activity becomes rewarding in itself. Usually parents and teachers encourage, cajole and/or strong-arm young children over these early periods, but without that external spur, the children may never get over the hump to where they want to do it for themselves – or, in other words, where the activity becomes intrinsically rewarding.

Knowing that your parents are fabulously wealthy can undercut these tough early stages of mastering a skill before it becomes intrinsically satisfying in itself. Why should I bother studying this stuff at university when I'm going to be rich anyway? they may think. People need the push of extrinsic motivation to get them to the point where they start to feel competent and intrinsically motivated. The age-old need to fend for yourself once you leave home provides that external kick of motivation to millions of children and adolescents throughout the world, but some offspring of the very successful just don't get that kick and so end up feeling demotivated and without direction in their lives.

Paulo Picasso may have become a feckless adult because he never got that push over the hump towards some area in which he could become self-motivated and feel competent. This was partly due to his being burdened with a great genius for a father, who had an abnormal personality and scarcely paid any attention to him, far less pushed him towards some motivating direction in life. But even when a rich parent does find time to give that essential motivation-building attention to a child, the looming presence of to-be-inherited millions can sabotage both the unwary parents' and their offspring's commitment to the child's climb up the hump of effort to the point where motivation becomes intrinsic and the drive for achievement is internalised.

Billionaires such as Microsoft founder Bill Gates have wisely foreseen the potentially demotivating curse that a huge inheritance can bring to a child. He has said that he will give his children some money but not a meaningful percentage of his fortune.[24] Gates and his wife have committed to giving away the majority of their wealth to good causes and have persuaded a number of other billionaires, including Warren Buffett and Facebook founder Mark Zuckerberg, to do the same.[25]

But is this notion of achievement motivation an open-and-shut case? Can we put Paulo Picasso's failure to achieve even modest success simply down to his father's failure to get him over the hump to self-motivated achievement? Not entirely – achievement motivation is not quite as simple as that.

Too much of a good thing

I overheard my fellow student 'Peter' one day talking to a girl. 'Peter' was talking intensely about how he wanted to make a fundamental discovery in science, one that would change the world. I had heard him say things like that before; it was as if he wanted to be another Darwin. Instead, within a year 'Peter' had dropped out of university – he seemed suddenly to have lost his motivation.

But, bright lad that he was, 'Peter' started working in a quite different domain, and within a few years he was near the top of that tree. But, on the infrequent occasions that I caught up with him, he exuded a sense of restlessness and discontent. He returned to university and completed a degree in yet another field, coming top of his class. He started working in that field, got a good job in a leading centre – but then dropped out and went back to one of his two previous areas of expertise.

'Peter' told me that when he astounded colleagues in one of his jobs by telling them he was leaving, his boss told him that 'Peter' had always seemed mildly depressed. And 'Peter' *was* mildly depressed, I suppose – constantly feeling that he had failed to meet the impossible target he had set himself of making a fundamental scientific breakthrough in biology.

It's not that he couldn't have done it if he had he stuck it out in one field – he was definitely intellectually capable of it. But in science, as in business, you can't plan for guaranteed success. There is a huge amount of luck attached to who ends up being a big winner, although persistence and determination can definitely reduce the odds: as the Hollywood producer Samuel Goldwyn once said: 'The harder I work the luckier I get.'

Keeping motivated, therefore, means enjoying the intrinsic satisfaction of mastering day-to-day challenges – like the Japanese students fired up to test their intelligence and earn purely symbolic points. If you focus only on a distant, enormous goal, then you will devalue your small everyday achievements and make them seem worthless.

That may be what happened to 'Peter' – the sense of restlessness he exuded came from the fact that his reward network was not fired up by the challenges of short- or even medium-term accomplishments because, compared with the enormous goal he had set himself, each of these was as worthless as a Lehman Brothers share certificate in late 2008. Little wonder he was chronically dissatisfied – every achievement was a failure in his eyes.

The eminent Harvard psychologist David McLelland studied the drive to achieve over many decades and discovered that the people who achieved most – the winners, in other words – tended to be those who, like Goldilocks, didn't like their porridge either too hot or too cold. The people who actually ended up achieving the most tended to set *moderately* challenging targets for themselves: that is, demanding but attainable.[26] Underachievement is almost inevitable if you set your sights so low that you don't expect to win. But setting them too high, as 'Peter' did, can have similarly disabling effects.

Children of very successful parents can find it very hard to get into ambition's Goldilocks zone. If your parents are geniuses, how do you avoid the shadow of their level of achievement? How can you set goals for yourself that don't look trivial and paltry compared with their great work? Even with a parent more attentive than Pablo Picasso, it is hard for the child of the very successful to make their own mark, and feel a sense of intrinsic accomplishment and competence at achievements which are more modest than those of their parent.

Paulo Picasso was not a winner in life. He presided over a suffering family and died a heavy drinker at fifty-four. Here was a family whose possible success in life was blighted by the withering shadow cast by the genius of the great painter.

Have we then solved the mystery of Picasso's son? Was he compelled to lose in life because his own achievements would always look meagre against the towering accomplishments of his father?

Perhaps this is part of the story – but if so, then all children of winners would end up as failures, and that simply is not the case. Something else must come into play as well. One possibility is that fame messes up families and that the disturbance of normal family relationships snuffs out the possibility of becoming a winner. Again there is something to this argument – certainly Pablo Picasso's multiple, complex families generated huge problems which reverberate to this day. But there are many successful people who have grown up in broken families, none more prominent than US President Barack Obama, whose Kenyan father abandoned his mother when the future president was a toddler. No, family fracture cannot entirely explain the mystery either.

What else could it be?

Hiding the ladder

Julius Caesar became absolute dictator of Rome in 47 BC, at the age of fifty-three. In spite of dictatorship being regarded in Roman law as a temporary position, Caesar went on to appoint himself dictator for life three years later, the event being commemorated with a statue to himself with the inscription 'The unvanquished demi-god'. He did not last long in that role: famously, on the Ides of March of that year, 44 BC, he was stabbed to death by a group of republican conspirators.

Sitting alone with his shotgun behind the barred windows of La Posta Vecchia, nibbling, it is said, on polenta and figs, J. Paul Getty not only said that he was *like* an emperor, he claimed that he *was* an emperor, the reincarnation of Hadrian, no less, the brilliant conqueror who built Hadrian's Wall in England and the Pantheon in Rome.

Ancient Rome was wary of living emperors who believed they were gods, as Julius Caesar found to his cost. They were right to be wary as it is the fate of emperors everywhere to fall into the trap of considering themselves as appointed by gods if not being gods themselves. In the miserable luxury of his lonely villa, would we be surprised if J. Paul Getty felt himself to be so special and all-powerful that he would have concluded that gods must be involved?

Marina Picasso recalls in her memoir how she, her brother Pablito and their father Paulo would make a weekly journey to La Californie, Pablo Picasso's sprawling house near Cannes, to seek cash for the family. But only sometimes were they admitted. Marina recalls being told on these occasions: 'The Sun cannot be disturbed.' It seems that the great artist was considered by his entourage as a god-like figure, if not a god himself – for what is the sun if not the essential, eternal source of energy for the world? Pablo himself, when contemplating his genius, more modestly referred to himself as El Rey – the King.

With a sun-god for a father, how could any son or daughter do anything but accept their insignificant place in such a solar system? Is this, then, the answer to the mystery of Pablo Picasso's son? Do children of 'emperors' feel crushed into insignificance by the seemingly god-given magnificence of a parent's achievements? For some – yes, but some children of life's significant winners do well, too, if not at quite the same levels as their parents. Lachlan Murdoch, son of the media emperor Rupert Murdoch, would be one example, as would Hans Einstein, son of Albert Einstein, who became an eminent hydraulic engineer. Both of these sons had rancorous and difficult relationships with their fathers but this did not eviscerate their lives in the way that Paulo Picasso's seems to have been.

Perhaps, then, it is something to do with how the child of the winner thinks about their parent's success? Clinical Psychologist Dr Fiona O'Doherty of the Beacon Hospital in Dublin has studied the phenomenon of underachievement in the children of highly successful parents.[27] She observed: 'Think of it this way: the child sees a parent high in the tree of success and wonders how he got there. The parent knows he has climbed up a difficult ladder, with many small steps, some of them luck, some perseverance and others to do with skill and application. But something happens to some successful people – they hide the ladder. By this I mean that, in the self-satisfaction of their success, they seek to be admired for their greatness and do not wish to see this "greatness" tarnished by the true picture of a thousand small steps up a shaky ladder.'

And what better way to hide the ladder can there be than to consider your achievements as god-given, or worse, that they can be explained only by your own god-like status? That is the delusion that many emperors, such as Julius Caesar, have fostered – witness Caesar's statue to the 'unvanquished god', J. Paul Getty's belief that he was a reincarnation of Hadrian, and Pablo Picasso calling himself 'the King'. So was Paulo Picasso doomed to failure because it seemed that his father's success emerged from god-given genius and was therefore, for him, unattainable? Perhaps, but it begs a question: why do some parents 'hide the ladder'?

'Terry' was, like 'Peter', another student at my university. 'Terry' did not look much different from the rest of us, but somehow everyone seemed to know and recognise him as he strolled around campus looking thoughtful. 'Terry' was a postgraduate student, but you never saw him in the library – he didn't seem to have to study. Everyone said it was because he was so bright.

Yet 'Terry' didn't do particularly well in the end – he did not end up as a high-flying professor, not even as a jobbing associate professor. 'Terry' went through life being . . . well, bright; he limped along fine but he didn't 'win' in any conventional sense of the word. So what happened? After all, wasn't 'Terry' born to win, with all his brightness? What happened that someone with so much promise did not succeed?

Before trying to unravel the reasons for 'Terry's destiny, let's consider 'Tony'. 'Tony' was a sixteen-year-old boy referred to a clinic where I was an intern clinical psychologist. He was a healthy-looking lad, strong and handsome, but with a somewhat hunted look. 'Tony' seemed pale and preoccupied and his eyes did not shine as they should, given his background and advantages, which were so much better than those of most of the children I saw in the clinic.

'Tony's model parents were also a little pale and definitely worried: after all, hadn't they come all the way here to bring their only son to a London psychology clinic? But what was the problem? Well, 'Tony' wasn't doing well at school, and he was morose and unmotivated. 'Tony' didn't take much part in the interview, sitting quietly, looking disengaged and rather sad.

I was, to be frank, at a bit at a loss with this case and unsure what to do. Indeed, was there anything that I could do? That was until his father let it slip out . . . but before I reveal what he said, let me ask you to take a trip back to your own childhood.

Think back to when you were at school. Read these questions and choose the answer under each question which best fits how you might have responded, to the best of your recollection.

1. When you find it hard to do arithmetic or mathematics, is it.
    a. *because you didn't study the subject hard enough?*
    b. *because the problems were too hard?*

2. When you do well on a test, is it
    a. *because you studied well for it?*
    b. *because the test was easy?*

3. When you get a better result in a test than you expected, is it
    a. *because you tried harder?*
    b. *because someone helped you?*

4. If you solve a problem quickly, is it
    a. *because you focused on it carefully?*
    b. *because it was an easy problem?*

5. When you forget something that the teacher told you, is it
    a. *because you didn't try hard enough to memorise it?*
    b. *because the teacher was bad at explaining it?*

6. Suppose someone doesn't think you are very bright, then
    a. *can you make him change his mind if you try?*
    b. *some people will think you're not bright no matter what you do?*

What did you, the child, answer? More of the *a* or more of the *b* alternatives? These questions are similar to those that Virginia Crandall and her colleagues from the Fels Research Institute in Ohio devised in 1965 to probe how children thought about their academic achievements.[28] But it was not until thirteen years later that the importance of these questions emerged. It is worth taking time to focus on the details of this research as it gives a powerful insight into our own childhood psychological make-up.

In 1978 Carol Diener and Carol Dweck of the University of Illinois used Crandall's questionnaire in a study of how children approach difficult problems.[29] They gave seventy eleven-year-olds a series of cards, on each of which were two figures, and they had to choose which figure was the correct solution to a puzzle which they had to deduce by trial and error over a sequence of cards. Each figure was composed of: an outside shape which could be a square or triangle; an inside shape which could be a dot or a star; and the figures could also be either red or blue. So, a child might decide that the 'rule' that determined the right answer was 'triangle', and would consistently choose the triangle answer, irrespective of what the colour and the inside shapes were. It's similar to those problem-solving puzzles that many IQ tests use. On page 36 you can see a picture of typical problems (with red and blue replaced by white and grey in the figure).

In the first row of the figure, if you decided that shape was the rule, then you might guess that the triangle was the correct shape. If that was the correct answer, then you would say 'left' for the first card, 'left' for the second, 'right' for the third and 'left' for the fourth. If on the other hand, you decided that colour was the rule to focus on, and that 'grey' was the correct answer (using grey and white instead of the red and blue of the original study), then you would say 'right' for the first, 'right' for the second, 'right' for the third and 'left' for the fourth. Finally, if you guessed that the dot/star was the key rule, and that 'star' correct choice, then you would say 'left', 'right', 'right', 'right'.

The children were trained to do the problems by the researcher giving them feedback after every card, and if necessary they were given a hint like: 'The correct answer is one of the two shapes, either the triangle or the square. See if you can figure out the right answer. The same answer is right for this whole deck of cards.' In the end all the children could complete the test by discovering the rule and the correct answer within the rule through trial and error by being told right or wrong after each answer. But then things got tricky.

Next the children were given a fresh set of twenty similar cards, but this time they were only told 'right' or 'wrong' after every fourth answer – so they did not receive any feedback for

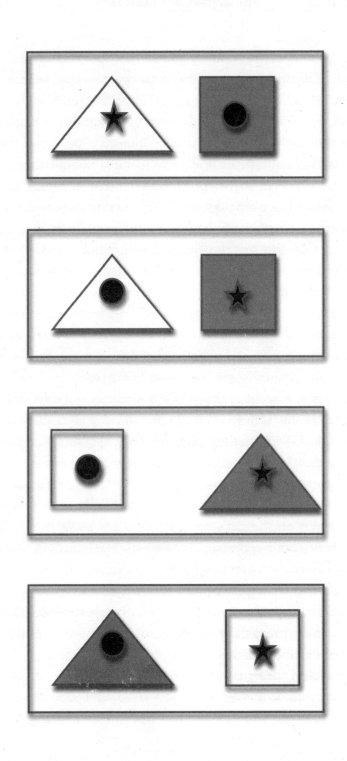

three-quarters of the cards, yet they still had to find the right answer. A twenty-card sequence was long enough for them to try out various different guesses about what the correct rule could be. All the children, it is important to remember, had learned successfully how to do this task in training – there were none who had been simply unable to do it. The only difference now was that they had to persevere with much less feedback, and guide themselves to the right solution over the twenty cards.

There are effective and ineffective strategies for solving problems like this. Julie sees the first card in the figure – a white triangle with a star in the middle on the left and a grey square with a dot in the middle on the right. She has to choose either the left or the right shape as the correct answer. If she thinks that colour is the rule dictating what is right or wrong, she may guess that grey is the correct answer and will always choose the shape that is grey. If she is told that she is wrong, as for very many things in life, she doesn't know *why* she is wrong. Maybe the rule *is* colour, and she has simply chosen the wrong colour. If that is the case, then she might try white in the next trial, or alternatively she could test the idea that it is the big shape that is the rule, and might point to the grey square on the next card. Failing that, she might focus her attention on the dot in the middle, and try to get correct answers by choosing on the basis of what the small shape is. Children who show effective problem-solving strategies try out ideas in this way until they start being told that they are correct.

Ineffective strategies, on the other hand, were ones which could never lead to a correct answer. For instance, James always chose white irrespective of feedback, Mary just alternated between left and right no matter what the feedback was, or Jack always picked the figure on the left.

Now think back to yourself as a child, and your answers to the six questions above. Were you more inclined to choose the *a* or the *b* answers? In the study, based on a bigger set of similar questions, if you had answered *a* a lot, Diener and Dweck would have classified you as 'mastery-oriented', while if you had tended to go for more of the *b* answers, they would have described you as 'helpless'. Which were you? – Whether you were an *a*- or *b*-answer child had a huge effect on how you would have performed for Diener and Dweck.

After 'failure' – i.e., being told an answer was wrong – children who gave more *a* answers switched more often to an effective strategy for solving the problem, while the *b*-answer – more 'helpless' – children acted like rabbits in the headlights and never improved their strategy. On the contrary, most of them worsened, moving to another ineffective strategy such as always sticking to the same shape, or just alternating left and right without taking heed of the feedback.

Remember, these 'mastery-oriented' and 'helpless' children had solved the tasks equally well during training – they were of the same mental ability; what distinguished them from one another was their response to failure. Asked after the end of the test why they thought they had had trouble with the problems, no less than half the *b*-answer children said, 'because I'm not smart enough'. How many of the *a*-answer children said this? None! Again, remember that there was *no* difference in how smart the two groups actually were.

And what did the *a*-answer, 'mastery-oriented' kids say when, after the test, they were asked, 'Why do you think you had trouble with the problems?' About a quarter said it was because they hadn't tried hard enough, a fifth put it down to bad luck, another fifth to the test being harder than the training one and another fifth said it was because the researchers had been unfair. None of them said it was because they weren't smart enough, unlike the *b*-answer children.

In a second study, the children were asked to speak out loud as they tried to solve the problems and again there were dramatic differences. More than half the 'mastery-oriented' children said things to themselves that could actually help them solve the problems, such as: 'The harder it gets, the harder I need to try' or 'I should slow down and try to figure this out.' The vast majority of the 'mastery-oriented' children said so-called 'self-monitoring' things to themselves such as 'I'm not concentrating', while none of them said demoralising things such as 'I give up', as several of the 'helpless' group did. The rabbit-in-the-headlights behaviour of the equally smart but 'helpless' children led them to say things to themselves which were irrelevant and actually stopped them from solving the problem.

In a second piece of research two years later[30] Diener and Dweck gave the same test to 'helpless' and 'mastery-oriented' children, but stopped half of them after they had just failed an item and half of them after they had just passed an item, to ask them some questions about how they thought they were doing. 'Helpless' children under-estimated how many successes they had had so far, and didn't see these successes as evidence of their ability – nor did they expect themselves to be successful in future problems. Failure left the 'mastery-oriented' children undaunted and optimistic about future performance.

But do these reactions to success and failure in classroom tests actually matter, and if so, can parents do anything about it? As we will see, they most certainly do, and yes, usually they can.

Here are a few more questions for you to answer. Assess how much you agree or disagree with each.

1. People have a more or less fixed quota of intelligence and can't change it much.
2. No matter how much you learn, you can't really change your intelligence.
3 People can work to improve their intelligence.
4. No matter how intelligent you already are, you can always improve it.

You will see that these questions have a lot in common with those the children solving the IQ-like problems answered. Dweck had narrowed down Crandall's questionnaire to this main issue – people's theory or belief about their intelligence. Using a few questions similar to the four above, she wanted to know how helpless people felt about their intellectual performance, versus how much mastery they felt they had over it. Another way of putting it is that some people saw their intelligence as an *entity* – a thing over which they had little or no control. Others, on the other hand, saw their intelligence in incremental terms. This entity-incremental distinction was very similar to the distinctions made by helpless and masterful children in the study by Diener and Dweck that I've just described.

Lisa Blackwell from Columbia University teamed up with Dweck and others to see whether these theories that people held about their own intelligence had any wider impact on their lives.[31] They followed almost 400 twelve- to thirteen-year-olds who were just embarking on their junior high school career. When Blackwell compared the progress of those children who saw their intelligence as a 'thing' with that of those who saw it as something 'incremental', she discovered something astonishing.

In September of the seventh grade, the two groups scored similarly on standard mathematics tests. By the spring of eighth grade, the children who believed that their intelligence was a 'thing' over which they had no control – irrespective of how intelligent they actually were – showed no change in their grades. The children who thought intelligence was something you could do something about, on the other hand, steadily increased their grades in mathematics.

This was true even with children who scored quite low in the mathematics test in their seventh grade – if they had an incremental theory of intelligence, they improved their test scores; on the other hand, even high-scoring children who believed intelligence to be a fixed entity flat-lined in their grades.

And that brings me back to what 'Tony's father had told me in the clinic that suddenly made me understand 'Tony's morose lack of motivation. His father said, 'The thing is, one day at an exhibition in our town, there was this Mensa stall, and "Tony" did an intelligence test – they told us he had a very high IQ and should come back for more testing.' Ah!

Mensa is the organisation for people who score in the top 2 per cent of certain IQ tests. If you are accepted into Mensa, you choose to label yourself, very publicly, as having a high IQ. And as for 'Terry', the postgraduate, guess what organisation he belonged to – *Mensa*. How do I, who only knew him because of his constant bright presence across university affairs, know this? Because if you hadn't heard how bright he was, he would make sure he casually mentioned his membership of Mensa.

Schoolboy 'Tony' was of slightly above average intelligence – I know because I gave him the Wechsler Intelligence Scale for Children, which is a very comprehensive, time-consuming face-to-face test that probes ability across a lot of different mental functions – but he wasn't by any means a super-intelligent boy. The test he did at the Mensa booth was a paper and pencil puzzle test parts of which may have had some similarities with Diener and Dweck's shapes test described above. His parents were told that this was just a screening test, and he should come back for testing that would properly establish their son's IQ, but all they heard was that their son was 'highly intelligent' and he did not go back as advised by the people at the Mensa booth. The trouble was, though he was moderately intelligent, he wasn't of exceptional IQ – and even if he had been, as we have seen, for many people it is not a good idea to be 'branded' in this way.

The consequences of this for 'Tony' were profound. The thing about IQ is that those academic psychologists who are most enthusiastic about it are, in the main, convinced that it is largely genetically inherited – in other words, an entity or endowed. And as Dweck's research has shown, once you start believing that your intelligence is endowed, you will tend to cope badly with failure compared with those who believe it's something incremental that can be worked on.

'Tony' continually disappointed his parents – and himself – by his totally reasonable but average performance at school. His parents' expectations for him built his supposed IQ into an entity – a basic feature of himself like his height, gender and looks. But what had become a fundamental aspect of his self-perception – 'I'm super-bright' – was bruised and battered every single day by the reality of his school performance and his disappointed parents' reaction to it. No wonder the poor lad looked so morose.

'Terry' was known for being bright, but if you asked other students how they knew this – had he written a ground-breaking academic paper or book, for instance? – a frown would come over the face of the person telling you and they would mutter something like, 'But he's in Mensa.' 'Terry' actually didn't achieve much because putting his vaunted IQ to the test was a huge risk. What if his hypothetical book didn't sweep the international stage? It would not just be a failure for his book – it would be a failure of a core feature of his self!

Martin Covington of the University of California at Berkeley has shown that people like 'Terry' who see their performance as a manifestation of this entity called intelligence tend to focus on 'performance' goals.[32] And the other name for this type of goal is an 'ego-goal'. For 'Tony' and 'Terry', their performance wasn't just a skill, like how well they played tennis – it was a central outcrop of their egos. Once intellect comes to be seen in this way, performance becomes a total risk – and it is the entire self-esteem that is being risked. No wonder 'Terry' shied away from ever putting his sparkling brightness to any real test. People like 'Terry' are constantly focused on beating others – on being first. It is the outcome they are concerned with, understandably enough, because every outcome is a public test of their ego. And if they cannot be sure of beating others, they shy away from the contest.

My successful fellow students who were not cursed by such entity-inspired ego-goals weren't performance-focused – they were 'learning-focused', in Covington's terms. Their goals came from the challenge of mastering the difficult problems they faced – they were the *a*-answer children who muttered to themselves, 'I'm not concentrating enough,' rather than something like, 'I'm no good at this.' When the tester said 'wrong' to them, as in Diener's study, they would have taken a deep breath and focused harder, maybe even with a glint in their eye.

'Terry' and 'Tony', on the other hand, would have been the *b*-answer 'helpless' schoolchildren in Diener's study: once the tester said 'wrong' to them, their hearts would have raced, their minds would have fogged over and the terrible, fearful thought would have welled up in their minds, 'Maybe I'm not smart!' 'Terry' might have responded randomly and then told the teacher that he was in Mensa; 'Tony' would probably have become even more morose and agonised over yet another blow to his fragile ego.

And had 'Terry' and 'Tony' been around for a brain-imaging study carried out by Jennifer Mangels and her colleagues at Columbia University,[33] we would have seen this ego-vulnerability at work in their brains. Electrical brain recordings were taken from two groups of students – one a *b*-answer, entity theory of intelligence group, and the other an *a*-answer, incremental theory of intelligence group.

One of the tests that we often give in my laboratory involves listening to a series of simple sounds and pressing a button when an occasional slightly different sound is heard. As we record your brain waves, that target sound will cause a big wave of brain activity towards the back of the brain – neuroscientists call that wave the 'P3b'. But from time to time we might sneak in a completely 'oddball' sound – like a strange crunching noise; in response to this sound, a different surge of activity courses through the brain, called the 'P3a wave'. This wave signifies a sort of *'Hold on, what the hell was that?'* brain response, and it happens particularly in the front of the brain.

Mangels and her colleagues gave the Columbia undergraduates a general knowledge test – 'What is the capital of Australia?' would be the sort of question posed – while they were hooked up to an EEG machine measuring the brain's electrical activity, and compared the two groups. And what happened when the students received feedback that a particular answer was wrong? The entity group showed a much bigger P3a wave, front-of-the-brain response than the incremental group – showing that for them this failure feedback was a real 'What the hell was that?' event. Here we could see the threat to their egos, acting out in brain activity.

But even more important was their response to helpful feedback – i.e., how their brains responded to the correct answer being flashed up – 'Canberra', in response to the Australia question, for instance. The incremental group's brains showed a big surge in brain activity that we know is linked to grabbing information and storing memory – encoding. This happens in the temporal lobes of the brain, along with parts of the frontal lobes.

The incremental group's brains soaked up the feedback hungrily and this paid off over the course of the general knowledge test, where they improved their scores because they were able to give the correct answer to some of the questions they didn't know the first time. But what about the entity group and their P3a-challenged egos? It seems that their brains were too caught up in the challenge to their egos produced by the 'wrong' response to fully soak up the feedback that would help them do better in the future. Their temporal-frontal memory *encoding* response was smaller than for the incremental group and also meant that they didn't learn as well from the feedback they got to their wrong responses.

So here we see why 'Terry' and 'Tony' did not thrive: finding out that they were wrong was such a challenge to their egos that it interfered with their brains' ability to learn from failure and improve their intellectual abilities. Yet there was nothing inevitable or 'hard-wired' about this response – it was just a belief – and beliefs can change, sometimes rapidly and easily. I told 'Tony' and his parents that while he was clever, he wasn't superbright, but that there was no reason he couldn't achieve highly in school with hard work and perseverance. His parents were a bit crestfallen, while 'Tony' looked a little shocked, then relieved; after a short while it looked like a weight had been lifted from his shoulders.

My 'therapy' for 'Tony' was simply to teach him the alternative *a*-answer belief about his abilities: I taught him an incremental view of his intellectual abilities – about effort and application and seeing difficulties as challenges. I think it began to work, but as I had to move on to a different clinic as part of my training, I don't know what happened in the longer term. But there is no reason why any child who holds an 'entity' theory of his or her abilities couldn't quite easily be taught to change to a more useful and less handicapping 'incremental' theory, where they learn to see how success is a product as much of what they *do* as what they *are*. 'Entity' thoughts such as 'I'm no good at maths' or 'I am no good at sports' need to be replaced by 'incremental' thoughts such as 'I didn't like maths at school and lost interest in it' or 'I need to find a sport that suits my abilities.'

'Terry' and 'Tony' had had a curse put on them – a handicapping belief about the immutability of their intellectual abilities. This is a common curse of modern times, and one which applies much more widely beyond the domain of intelligence – it is the dead weight of 'genetic fatalism'.

The curse of genetic fatalism

The sequencing of the human genome has accelerated the spread of a core belief of our time – that much of what we are and do is coded in our genes; it is a form of biological predestination. Most geneticists are cautious about claims made about the extent to which complex behaviours and personal characteristics are determined by genes. There are only 20–30,000 of the things, and that is an impossibly small number to control all the glorious manifestations of human behaviour. And we evolved genetically in order to learn from the environment, so wise geneticists will make the case for nature *with* nurture, rather than for nature *versus* nurture.

But there are psychologists and psychiatrists who, for many different reasons, choose to greatly exaggerate how things like psychological problems, personality and intelligence are influenced by genes. Yes, there are genetic contributions to many of these, but in very few of them are genes the only or even main determining factor. But the problem with believing that genes call the shots where intelligence, personality and psychological problems are concerned, is that it leaves you, as the human actor in this drama, helpless. There is nothing you can do about the genes, but if you choose to believe eminent academics that your behaviour is largely genetically determined, then that belief is likely to become a self-fulfilling prophecy.

We saw how 'Terry' and 'Tony' were disabled by an 'entity' notion of their intellectual abilities, and how a genetically fatalist belief can actually interfere with a child's learning if and when they come across even a minor setback or failure. Whatever we do, we should not praise a child for being 'bright', but rather for their effort, perseverance or ingenuity, otherwise we risk imposing the curse of genetic fatalism on them.

Rather than praise them for being bright, we should praise them for 'grit'. Angela Duckworth and her colleagues from the University of Pennsylvania discovered that the quality of 'stickability' and perseverance was a highly significant factor in Ivy League undergraduate exam performance and even spelling ability in seven- to fifteen-year-old children.[34] Their measure of 'grit' had two elements – consistency of interests over time and perseverance of effort. The sort of consistency questions were similar to this: 'I find it hard to follow up on projects which last for more than a few months.' Examples of the perseverance questions were similar to this: 'Whatever I start I usually complete, I work hard or I don't get discouraged by setbacks.' Children and adults who were high on these grit items were more likely to be winners than those with less grit.

In short, the curse of genetic fatalism undermines grit, and grit is one of the most important ingredients in life – not just in academic achievement, but in work, relationships and coping with stress and illness.

Science is getting close to having a brain-imaging method for detecting a type of pathology in the brain that is closely linked to Alzheimer's Disease – deposits called amyloid plaques and neurofibrillary tangles. It will not be long before, if we have worries about our memory, we will be referred for scans which will tell us whether we have one of these key elements of Alzheimer's Disease. Hopefully this will then allow scientists to develop new treatments which can halt the disease early on and stop it in its tracks before too much damage is done to the brain. The problem is that at the moment there is no treatment with big beneficial effects and so being given the diagnosis is a pretty depressing experience.

But are things as simple as that? David Bennett and colleagues at Rush University Medical Centre in Chicago followed a group of older people, having measured their memory and cognitive abilities while alive.[35] After their eventual death, they measured the amount of Alzheimer's-type damage to their brains. Now, we might expect that their memory and mental abilities while alive might be linked to the amount of pathology in their brains. They were – but not for everyone.

In older people who were relatively isolated, namely who had the smallest number of family and close friends whom they saw at least once a month, those with more pathology in their brains had had poorer mental function while alive. But this was *not* true for those who had the richest social networks of friends and family – in them there was *no* relationship between the 'gunk' in their brains and their mental abilities while alive.

What seems to be happening is that the mental challenge, stimulation and morale that comes from having friends and family around us allows the brain to keep functioning pretty well *in spite of* the pathology. The brain is hugely plastic, at any age, and the Alzheimer's pathology may have less effect on a brain which is stimulated and hence better connected by a rich social network. It's not that having friends and family around cured the Alzheimer's Disease – certainly not – but they allow people to function better mentally in spite of the changes in the brain.

If I had been one of the first people to receive the new brain-imaging test for early Alzheimer's Disease, before any pharmacological treatment had been developed for it, there would have been a terrible temptation to succumb to the depressing and fatalistic curse that my fate is sealed and there is nothing I could do about it. But that is not necessarily the case. Even where our abilities are very strongly influenced by our biology – as in Alzheimer's Disease – our brains are too complex for it ever to be a cut-and-dried case justifying our mentally shutting up shop and giving up.

So fatalism – genetic or biological – can cripple us and in many cases is not scientifically justified. But lots of people handicap themselves by assuming that their personality and behaviour are 'entities' which are largely outside their control. And if we believe they're outside of our control, for sure we won't be able to control them.

Carol Dweck,[36] for instance, has shown that children who suffer a rejection by other children in a new school are much more likely to withdraw into themselves and avoid trying again if they think that the failure was because of something *inside* them: if they think 'I'm no good at getting on with other kids' (an 'entity' theory) rather than 'They're a real clique – I should try someone else' (an incremental theory), then they can go into a spiral of social rejection. And they can end up being consistently unpopular because they *avoid* doing the things that could make them accepted – all because they are handicapped by a helplessness-inducing fatalism about the essentially immutable nature of their abilities and characteristics.

Genetic fatalists, in short, believe that they have a fixed 'dose' of attributes – intelligence, ability, personality, self-control, happiness and this belief or 'attribution' automatically undermines any attempts they might make to change or improve themselves; hence it sabotages their ability to win. Being the son of the 'Sun' Pablo Picasso is profoundly disabling, because how could a 'Sun-genius' be anything other than born, not made? For Paulo, his father's success had nothing to do with apparently irrelevant facts such as that Pablo's father was an art teacher and that when he was a child he did little else but draw and paint – thousands and thousands of hours of obsessed, focused practice.

Being the son or grandson of the reincarnation of Hadrian must have been equally disabling for the Gettys. What hope is there of ever succeeding in your own right if the great man considered the possibility that his successes might have been an outcrop of supernatural forces?

As Anders Ericsson at Florida State University has argued, genius only begins after 10,000 hours of practice.[37] Of course there are some inherited and environmental advantages for most high performers, but without practice and perseverance you will never get a genius – whether it be a Mozart, a Rostropovich, an

Einstein or a Picasso. These 10,000 hours are the rungs of the ladder that some 'geniuses' draw up behind them, 'hiding the ladder', in Fiona O'Doherty's terms, and hence crippling their children.

Earlier I asked the question, why do successful parents often hide the ladder? The first answer is that they attribute their success to something inside themselves – an entity, in other words. They contemplate their sparkling success in the world and can only assume that they have been born geniuses – in other words, by believing in genetic (or god-given) fatalism, they have no choice but to hide the ladder – because in their eyes there was no ladder helping them to their greatness.

The curse of the parental ego

But there is a second reason why some parents 'hide the ladder' – something to which fathers are more susceptible than mothers. This concerns the distorting effect that success can have on the ego, inflating the self-importance of the parent to the point that he cannot bear the thought that luck or brute effort might have played a part in his dizzying climb to success. No, for such egos, the last thing they need to hear is that such success is potentially open to their offspring through such mundane recipes as hard work and looking for the lucky break: for an ego which has come to believe that their genius is an 'entity', to preserve that ego means denying the ladder of mundane effort and attributing success to genes or gods.

The seductive delusion of god-given genius is the psychological fate that binds together Pablo Picasso and J. Paul Getty. It is a terrible curse to have a god for a father.

But why does success breed such egos? As this chapter has shown, winners are certainly not necessarily born, so that raises the question as to whether success is an outcrop of circumstance – of chance events that shape our fates. That brings us to the Puzzle of the Changeling Fish.

2

The Puzzle of the Changeling Fish

Is winning a matter of chance and circumstance?

In the warm, shallow waters of Lake Tanganyika in East Africa, the African male cichlid fish, *Haplochromis burtoni*, comes in two types. One of these – the T fish – is blue or yellow and piratically striped with a thick black band across the eyes. The second type – the NT fish – is dowdy grey and nondescript, very similar in colouring to the females of the species.

As befits the 'good catch' that any prospective cichlid mother-in-law would desire for her daughter, the average T fish is very well endowed and highly attractive to females. He is also very aggressive to NT fish: why shouldn't he be, given his superior breeding?

The NT fish, on the other hand, is submissive and infertile – he lurks in the shadows, cloaked in anonymity with his shrunken, useless testes. Meanwhile T-überfisch struts his underwater stuff, spreading his precious, high-value DNA into a grateful gene pool. A good thing too, any self-respecting 'born to win' eugenicist might think to himself. 'I'm forever warning about the looming disaster due to biologically inferior human beings breeding too fast,' he might reflect, feeling that glow of lonely courage that comes from defying a political correctness that simply does not understand biology and evolution. 'Humans could learn a thing or two from the cichlid fish.'

Here, surely, is a striking example of the ruthless efficiency of evolution – the finest of the species have, through their selected fitness and good breeding, become hereditary lords of their territories, and of course in all such hierarchies the lords have their vassals – in this case the NT fish.

But haven't I misplaced this story? Shouldn't it have appeared in the previous, 'born to win', chapter? Are we not back to the 'born to win' notion, with the T cichlid fish showing that some cichlids are to the manor born, and that the rest are genetically predestined to skulk on the margins? Maybe – except for one thing: sometimes, something very, very strange happens.

From time to time, over the course of a few hours, a peculiar transformation comes over an NT fish: gradually his dull greyness is replaced by the glow of a gorgeous aquamarine or sunburst yellow. And as he gradually dons the colours of the T fish, his testes grow and surges of testosterone cause a dramatic change in his personality – the mild-mannered Dr Jekyll of Robert Louis Stevenson's famous novel turning into a medically engineered, dangerous and predatory Mr Hyde. Newly fertile, he becomes an aggressive rake of a fish, turning female heads and sending his former NT companions scurrying from his path. And there follows the sweet taste of revenge on his erstwhile T fish bullies, for whose females he now competes on an equal par.

What on earth is going on here? The T cichlid and the NT cichlid fish are still the same species and their transformation happens in a matter of hours. Here is what happened: something caused a group of cells in his brain to swell to eight times their previous, NT, size. And these cells ooze a certain sex hormone called gonadotropin-releasing hormone – it is this substance that causes the magical transformation in colour, testes size, personality and fertility. Sometimes, though less often, the reverse happens – a strutting T fish finds himself losing his colour and is dismayed to find his macho fish-hood shrink to almost nothing. What is going on here? What causes these changes? Is it something he ate? Some sort of fishy menopause? Or chemical or temperature change in the African waters? Or has there been some other random change in the circumstances in which this fish lives?

Of course, adult humans do show remarkable transformations, if not quite as dramatic as those of the NT fish. What causes these transformations? Are the changes themselves genetically predestined? This is pretty unlikely – some change in environment or circumstance would seem to be a much more plausible reason for an adult human to show big changes. That brings us to the question at the centre of this chapter: do changes in our environment determine whether we will be winners or losers? Are chance experiences and circumstance the things that make us winners or losers?

To answer that question, let's go to the floor of a London financial institution, where currency, bonds, commodities and futures are traded.

The year 2006 must seem like a distant, happy but fantastic dream to the traders and bankers of the post-2008 crash. There had been some hiccups – the portentous collapse of Enron among them – but 2006 was a time of plenty for the world, and particularly for the Gucci-clad, Porsche-driving traders of New York and London.

But the life of a trader is never without its ups and downs, and their fortunes and their lifestyles depended on the then relatively gentle oscillations of the market. It was during this pre-Lehman, pre-apocalyptic time of relative financial peace that a group of

Cambridge scientists decided to study a group of seventeen male London traders as they placed their bets on the markets.

The researchers measured testosterone levels each morning and afternoon for eight days. The seventeen traders had some high-testosterone mornings, and some low ones and on average they made a profit on high days and not on lows. Testosterone thus made the traders more adventurous and combative, and this style yielded them higher profits, bigger bonuses and perhaps a contribution to the cost of their next Porsche.

Testosterone is a hormone which boosts men's and women's sex drive and makes them more aggressive, and it does so by changing the chemistry of their brains.[1] But remarkably, as the Cambridge scientists showed, it also seems to be linked to *winning*: higher morning testosterone levels in the traders predicted higher profits on their day's trading. Testosterone appeared to increase their appetite for risk – and hence their likelihood of snatching a daring profit.

Were the successful traders like T cichlid fish – pushy, aggressive, risk-ready and successful in their brightly coloured neckties and suspenders? Yes, and what's more, they seemed to fluctuate from day to day in these characteristics, albeit in a less dramatic way than the T cichlid fish, though who knows, maybe the neckties were more dowdy on the profitless days.

So yes, the T cichlid fish mystery seems to have human parallels. But *why* do we – both men and women – get these big fluctuations in testosterone and all that goes with them? We need a quick trip back in time to a famous World Cup soccer match to answer that.

The Rose Bowl in Pasadena, California, was the scene of the World Cup Final between Brazil and Italy on 17 July 1994. It was a contest of enormous importance to the two nations. Italy had famously been knocked out of the previous semi-final, in Rome in 1990, when their hero Roberto Baggio kicked the last ball over the net during the penalty shoot-out, causing them to lose 4–3 to Brazil. Bad though this was for Baggio, that year's cup was a lot worse for Colombia's Andrées Escobar, whose team left the tournament after a first-round defeat on 22 June by the USA because he scored an own goal: he was shot dead outside a bar in Medellín ten days after his team's return home in disgrace. In sport, people take winning very, very seriously.

So, for the hundreds of millions of Italians and Brazilians who watched the match that sweltering Sunday, this was a very personal matter of wanting, often desperately, their team to win. Researchers from Georgia State University took testosterone measures from the saliva of some Brazil fans watching the match in a sports bar, and from Italian fans following it in a nearby pizzeria.[2] Immediately after the game – which Brazil won on penalties – they measured it again. The average testosterone levels of the Brazilian fans increased by 28 per cent, compared with a 27 per cent *decrease* in the Italian men.

The two nationalities behaved differently too. Some Brazilians were arrested for riotous celebration in the streets while the Italian men looked depressed and apathetic. Disheartened by the loss, several had to be pursued into the parking lot by the experimenters to collect post-game samples. 'Testosterone, and the feeling of power associated with it, increases as subjects bask in reflected glory and decreases as they experience vicarious defeat,' the researchers concluded.[3]

That is the first clue to solving the puzzle of the T cichlid fish and the London traders – does *winning itself* lead to the testosterone surges that remodel body, mind and behaviour? Before paying another visit to our T fish, let's take a trip to a boxing arena in Philadelphia.

Mike Tyson's tomato cans

It is 19 August 1995 and Mike Tyson feels the hot insistence of
dry desert air on his cheek for just the few seconds it takes him
to transit from his limousine to a side door of the MGM Grand
Arena in Las Vegas. Inside, 17,000 fans roar – they are going to
enjoy themselves for the then eye-watering $45.95 cost of their
tickets. This will be Tyson's first appearance since being paroled
after three long years in jail for the rape of an eighteen-year old
woman. Even for that few seconds he can hear it, that nervy,
party hum of Las Vegas must unsettle a man whose previous
partying got him into such trouble.

His opponent, Boston-Irishman Peter McNeeley, edgily skips
and jabs in the corner of the ring, hoping no doubt that three
years of prison food and harsh neon light will have bled some
aggression from his opponent's muscles. But the blast of howls
and whoops that ushers Tyson down the aisle towards him is
nevertheless daunting.

The bell rings and McNeeley is out, fists flailing – 'a dervish
with a death wish' as the famous Scottish sports journalist
William McIlvanney described him – and in spite of Tyson's
clumsy and ill-timed punches, it takes only eighty-nine seconds
for McNeeley to be disqualified because his manager illegally
squirms through the ropes in a mad attempt to protect his beaten
protégé.[4] The crowd howls their rage and disappointment.

It's 16 December 1995. This time it is the raw, wet cold of the
East Coast that rasps across Tyson's face as he transits from his
limo to the CoreStates Spectrum Arena in South Philadelphia,
where his second post-jail opponent awaits him, one Buster
Mathis, Jr. This time the fight lasts three rounds. As McIlvanney
sourly observes, 'Tyson was more likely to be disconcerted by a
slap from pendulous breasts than hurt by occasional flurries of

feather-duster hooks.' That it took Tyson until the last minute of the third round to dispatch his overweight opponent was an embarrassment that even the ebullient promoter Don King could not completely finesse.

It is obvious why King would not have wanted Tyson to restart his fight career with a competition against a reigning champion. But surely these two matches against 'tomato cans' – as such patsies are known in boxing – were more likely to trigger derision rather than acclaim for the former champion? And would not that derision weaken his self-belief and risk the renewal of his career?

King's long, colourful experience in the fight industry and his raw gut instinct knew better. But why? To answer that question entails a journey back to 1951 Chicago.

The end of the Second World War caused many to wonder what makes human beings tick and in particular why some try to dominate others. By the dawn of the new decade in 1950, Professor H. G. Landau of the University of Chicago was turning his mind to what it was that made animals form themselves into hierarchies. Most species, from hens to humans, organise themselves like this, and Landau's question was, why?

With Adolf Hitler barely five years dead, the Third Reich's toxic hierarchies could not have been far from the minds of the committee who decided to fund Landau's research. And, given the blind obedience to authority and ensuing bestiality that were all too vivid in the memories of those who had survived the war, his fascination with pecking orders no doubt seemed very relevant both to recent history and to 1950, since Stalin's Soviet Union dictatorship had exploded its first nuclear weapon the year before.

Hitler corrupted Darwinian evolutionary theory into a savage ideology that led to the extermination of the racially and biologically 'unfit'. But his was an extreme outcrop of a more general Western 'eugenicist' approach to human life which, though much less pernicious than its Nazi cousin, still had as its underlying assumption that hierarchies or classes were largely due to differences in inherited abilities. Just as hens had a pecking order that was obvious, natural and beneficial to the efficient running of the coop, so, the conventional pre-war thinking went, it went for human hierarchies and classes. 'Born to win' played very big to pre-war audiences outside of the Soviet bloc.

Professor Landau was a biologist who set about figuring out the mathematics of hierarchy. He published his first paper early in 1951: 'On dominance relations and the structure of animal societies: I. Effect of inherent characteristics', in the *Bulletin of Mathematical Biophysics*.[5] As is clear from the title, his first attempt at explaining the emergence of stable hierarchies or pecking orders based itself on 'inherent characteristics' – namely features like size, height, 'concentration of sex hormone' (e.g., testosterone levels) and other largely inherited qualities that should put us on a particular level in the natural social hierarchy.

Landau worked through his calculations and came to the conclusion that hierarchies are very unlikely to emerge when there is *just* a spread of inherent/inherited characteristics across a field of hens or a village of people. Different patterns of stable abilities and propensities across people did not on their own lead to hierarchies. No, to explain hierarchies you need something else, and that something was what Don King and his promoter friends stumbled upon decades later.

Professor Landau's second paper[6] was entitled 'On dominance relations and the structure of animal societies: II. Some effects of possible social factors' and it was here that he discovered that a hierarchy will appear if winning a challenge with another animal boosts your chances of winning the next encounter. Professor

Landau had – purely using statistical and mathematical models – discovered the 'winner effect.' He was too careful a scientist to speculate on why it might be that winning a fight would increase the chances of being victorious in a subsequent one. All he could say was that a rule was needed in order to explain how hierarchies would arise and be maintained over time.

It was a few years before biologists began to see in experiments what Landau had predicted from his mathematical equations.

While it is unlikely that boxing managers across the world had followed Professor Landau's work closely, nevertheless Don King had arranged that on 16 March 1996 Mike Tyson was again breathing the dry, warm desert air in Las Vegas, beneath the roaring lion of the MGM Grand Arena. This time, there were no 'tomato cans' – he would be fighting the WBC World Champion, Londoner Frank Bruno. And Tyson knocked him out in the third round, the parolee becoming world champion again. Landau's mathematically derived prediction of the existence of a 'winner effect' came to glossy realisation amid the sparkling neon of Las Vegas. Had scientific evidence caught up with Professor Landau's mathematics?

It had, but it took seventeen years from Landau's post-war studies before Arthur McDonald of the University of South Dakota tested Landau's hypothesis by studying the behaviour of the notoriously aggressive green sunfish.[7] First he watched carefully a group of these fish for three days and worked out which were the dominant and which the submissive fish on the basis of their various interactions with one another. He then divided the dominant fish into three groups: one went into isolation for five days, while another group was put into a tank with a larger fish and the final set were put in with smaller fish.

After five days the fish were put back into their original tank and their attack behaviour studied. And just as Landau had predicted, the dominant fish who had spent five days with the bigger fish were much less likely to attack and beat fish than before their stressful 'loser' experience. Their friends who had been with the smaller fish, on the other hand, came back into the real fish world fired up and aggressive, more dominant than before.

This is pretty much what Don King had arranged for Mike Tyson – McNeeley and Mathis were the small fish used to boost Tyson's winner effect and help win him back his world title. Landau was indeed right. And many other experiments followed with other species. A typical experiment put pairs of male mice into the mouse equivalent of the boxing ring, and the researchers rigged an otherwise equal contest by slipping a little sedative into one of the animal's pre-match food. Unsurprisingly, the non-sedated competitor would win but the consequences of this rigged match only emerged in the next bout. When the rigged-match winners were now pitted against a tough, unsedated and hard-eyed opponent, they were more likely to win this real fight than if they had not had the previous victory experience against the sedated mouse.

But while the winner effect was discovered in species after species, there was a problem – what caused it? It was not long before scientists started to measure the 'sex hormones' which Landau had only considered as 'inherent', or pre-existing factors. But hormones don't sit in our bodies like milk in the jug: hormones and behaviour are intimately linked, and it became clear that not only did hormones shape behaviour – *behaviour* changed hormone levels.

Study after study showed that winning caused a surge in testosterone, and that this was a major reason why animals were more likely to win their next, non-rigged fight: the testosterone surge made them less anxious, more aggressive, and gave them a higher pain threshold. Testosterone made them mean – and tough.

It is pretty obvious why testosterone should be important when trying to knock another man unconscious – but is it relevant to more civilised pursuits? Is it really relevant to everyday life, at home or in the office? Professor Alan Mazur of Syracuse University helped to answer that question by studying one of the most civilised and apparently gentle of human activities.

Mazur and his colleagues coaxed sixteen chess players from a city chess club to spit into saliva sample bottles before, during and after their matches at an important tournament and analysed the testosterone.[8] They found that testosterone levels surged among winners. What's more, those who had shown the biggest surges *before* the tournament were more likely to win – just like the London financial traders.

The winner effect is not confined to violent challenges then. In our daily lives, we – men in particular, but more on that later – are constantly challenging and competing with one another other. And how we come out of these challenges depends not just on our state of mind and hormonal activity before the event, but also on whether or not we have won in the past: few of us have a Don King giving us 'tomato cans', unequal fights which will give us a testosterone-fuelled advantage against the Frank Brunos of our lives.

When the mouse, boxer or chess player wins his rigged bout, the surge of testosterone that is triggered by this victory somehow carries forward to his next bout against a real, tough opponent days, weeks or months later. The winner's hormonal surge primes an aggressive fighting spirit that boosts his chance of winning a real fight. So the mismatched boxing bout between Tyson and his 'tomato cans' seems to be explained – except that we are still left with a puzzle of how a surge of testosterone following a single victory can have effects that last for months. How exactly did the winner-effect testosterone help Tyson win his bout?

The winner's brain

The California mouse, *Peromyscus californicus*, is a feisty beast, monogamous and as territorial as the cichlid fish. And he, like Mike Tyson, is a sucker for the winner effect, being more likely to win a big contest if he has just won an easier fight. But for the curious scientist he also offers one distinct advantage over studying Tyson – you can examine what is going on in his brain as the winner effect takes hold.

Matthew Fuxjager and his colleagues at the University of Wisconsin in Madison let male mice chalk up three wins against other mice and then after a fourth win, studied how many androgen receptors there were in key parts of their brains. Androgen receptors are receiving stations for testosterone, and the more there are of them, the more powerfully will any single spurt of testosterone affect the brain.

Fuxjager and his team discovered that winning a series of contests *boosted* the number of androgen receptors in a part of the brain that controls social aggression. It also increased the number of these receptors in parts of the brain's reward and motivation network called the nucleus accumbens and the ventral tegmental area. But then Fuxjager and his colleagues discovered something quite strange.

The California mouse is not only faithful and feisty, he is, it appears, a homebody also. Fuxjager discovered that the mouse showed a Tyson-type winner effect *only* after besting opponents on his home territory. Contests won away from his home turf did not help him in subsequent contests. What was going on here?

Another glimpse into the brain of the California mice gives us a clue. While the androgen receptors in the social aggression part of the brain blossomed after *all* the victories, whether on home ground or away from home, this was not true of the androgen receptors in the motivation parts of the brain. Only after the *home* victories did they swell in number, and not after away-match triumphs. What's more, it was only the brain-motivation area changes that correlated with the ability to win.

Winning then – but only at home – reshaped the structure and chemistry of the mice's brains; but it did not do this by simply turning up raw aggression in the brain, but by also swelling the motivational circuits and upping the will to fight.

It may seem strange that where you happen to be located determines what changes happen in the brain, and peculiar that Fuxjager's mice should only show these crucial brain changes when they fought at home. But something similar happened during the Vietnam War, where it was estimated that the majority of US service personnel had used heroin and one in five of them were addicted to it. A feared epidemic of returning drug addicts did not transpire[9] and most of the addicts did not remain addicted once back home in America. This was a major headache for experts in addiction, who regarded heroin addiction as a biologically determined disease that, once established, was very difficult to eradicate.

Shephard Siegel of McMaster University in Canada solved this problem.[10] He studied addiction in rats, and he knew that as animals and humans get addicted, their 'tolerance' to the drug increases, such that they need higher and higher doses to

achieve the same effect. His addicted rats could 'tolerate' enormous levels of heroin which would kill a non-addicted rat. What
puzzled Siegel, given this fact, was how many human heroin
addicts were dying of heroin overdoses – this shouldn't happen
if they were addicts whose bodies had developed tolerance to the
drug.

Siegel's breakthrough was to make rats addicted and tolerant
to heroin in a particular environment – a cage in a room with
its own colour and smells. Once they could take huge amounts
of heroin without harm, he then gave the rats a huge test dose –
half of them in the same room where they had become addicted,
and the other half in a different room with a different colour and
smells. The results were astounding: while one third of the rats
given the high test dose in the *same* room died of an overdose,
two thirds of those tested in the different room died. Just changing the environment *doubled* the death rate. The most fundamental of biological processes – a body's reaction to a deadly
drug – could be shaped by learning and environment, Siegel
showed.

And this answered Siegel's question about the overdoses
among human addicts: if an addict usually takes a drug in a
particular setting – say, his bedroom – then his body will learn
that his bedroom is the 'cue' to expect heroin to enter the bloodstream, and will trigger a physiological compensatory, opposite
effect to the expected effects of the drug, thus counteracting the
drug's effect on the brain. This is not at all what the addict wants
– he wants a high – so he has to increase his doses to continually
try to stay ahead of this high-busting wave of opposite bodily
and brain effects.

But suppose the addict needs to go out to find more heroin,
and because of the urgency of his need, ends up buying some
from a pusher and then going somewhere unusual to take his fix

– say, the bathroom of a cheap hotel. This, according to Siegel, is the equivalent of giving the rat a high dose of heroin in a different-coloured room. So the poor addict takes a dose of heroin no bigger than any he has taken before, but falls into a coma and is discovered by some distressed guest a few hours later. The new setting for taking drugs – an unfamiliar bathroom with different sight, sound and smell 'cues' – has left his body unprepared – intolerant – to the drug, which surges through his veins and kills him.

The homecoming Vietnam servicemen departed from their own strange and stressful environment. Their 'room' where they became addicted was the heat, the fear, the sights, the noise and the smell of Vietnam at war. They returned to a home environment so different that it had none of the 'cues' linked to their heroin addiction. Not only was their tolerance to heroin gone, we should infer from Siegel's research, but so also was the craving that is the dark underbelly of tolerance. They had, in short, left their addiction behind in the humid paddy fields of Vietnam, like the shed skin of a deadly snake.

Siegel's research shows us that the very chemistry of our bodies is tuned to the physical, social and psychological environment. Could this also be true for the chemistry of winning? Was Mike Tyson's testosterone-fuelled winner effect another example of brain and body chemistry being shaped by environment?

Fuxjager's brilliant study showed that it was: not only was brain chemistry shaped by winning in the home environment – brains were changed and androgen receptors were *created*. If a new stem-cell therapy had achieved this, it would have been in headlines throughout the world and the Nobel Prize would have been on everyone's lips.

In the battlefields of Vietnam and in the boxing rings of Las Vegas, brains are reshaped as if by stem-cell therapy. But it is underpinned by a strange type of chemistry – a sort of *chameleon* chemistry – the very matter of the brain being shaped by environment. Our brains are precisely shaped by the physical, social and psychological world we inhabit.

And that answers the second question about the winner effect – why should the effects of Tyson's defeat of McNeeley and Mathis carry over all those months until the Bruno fight? If we can generalise from Fuxjager's work, it seems that these 'tomato can' defeats may have physically reshaped Tyson's brain, increasing androgen receptors in the motivation parts.

Any contest triggers testosterone, be it boxing or chess. So, when Tyson came to fight Bruno, of course the usual surge of testosterone flooded both men's brains. But Tyson's brain – if Fuxjager's work applies to humans – may have sprouted extra receptors that sucked up the testosterone and magnified its effect on his brain and on his appetite for the fight.

The winner effect, then, almost certainly does not work by simply maintaining super-high levels of testosterone until the next contest – winners would likely suffer damage to their heart or risk injury because of their aggressive demeanour. Yes, winning boosts testosterone levels and may leave them in the long term somewhat higher than before. But the real effect of winning is in physically shaping the brain, so that the brain behaves like a turbo-charged car that pushes out more power for the same amount of gasoline.

But these changes are *context dependent*. Context means place – sights, sounds, smells like those of the White Room or the Vietnam rainforest – and for Mike Tyson it probably included the sounds and smells of the boxing ring. Context also means people – the presence of a partner, of an enemy, of a boss – or of an entire institution like a company or a school. But perhaps most of all, context means the *mental landscape,* the beliefs, emotions, feelings – some conscious, most unconscious – that encompass the event or the contest.

This is a truly fundamental discovery: we are totally connected with the world around us, shaped by and linked to its changing landscape right down to the very proteins expressed by our genes. Winning is just one important outcome of the shifting patterns of a web of interconnections between our brains and the surrounding world. And before you decide what to wear tomorrow morning, consider this next aspect of the environment which might affect your success tomorrow.

When, at the 2004 Olympic Games in Athens, Viktor Zuyev of Belarus climbed into the ring to fight for the gold medal against Odlanier Solís from Cuba, he was oblivious to the disadvantage he was under. Solís won the match 22 points to 13, and stood proudly on the dais to hear his country's national anthem play, while Zuyev stood downhearted one step below, clutching his silver medal. The handicap was the shirt he was wearing.

Zuyev had been allocated a blue shirt, not because blue matched his Nordic eyes, but because he had been randomly assigned that colour by the Games's organisers. His opponent had been lucky enough to get the red shirt: in boxing, as well as taekwondo, Greco-Roman wrestling and freestyle wrestling, Olympic opponents wore red or blue shirts at random.

Russell Hill and Robert Barton of the University of Durham in England made the discovery about shirt colours when they studied the results of Athens's Olympics bouts in these blue-red sports. Hill and Barton were able to look just at bouts between competitors of roughly equal ability – this was possible by looking at their pre-Olympics rankings. And when they did this, an astonishing fact emerged: red-shirted competitors won 62 per cent of the time, compared with only 38 per cent of the blue-shirted competitors.[11]

This was not a fluke, because Hill and Barton went on to look at soccer. In soccer tournaments, teams sometimes have to change their usual shirt colour if it is too similar to that of the team they are playing against. This let Hill and Barton look at how teams fare when they are wearing one colour – red in particular – versus any other colour. They did this in the Euro 2004 international soccer tournament and – surprise, surprise – teams did better and scored more goals when they were wearing red.

To understand how to explain this, imagine for a moment watching two men eyeballing each other, squaring up aggressively. One man's face is very red, while the other man's face is very white. What should we conclude about the relative mental states of the two men? Most people would assume that the red-faced man is angry and the white-faced one frightened. Our genetic ancestors, who were adept at recognising these signals, could use them to dominate and beat a frightened, pale-faced adversary. This would not only ensure the victor's survival to fight again, but also would give him better access to females and therefore a greater chance of passing on his genes.

And so it is that the colour red seems to be wired into our genes – just wearing that colour puts an opponent at a disadvantage because of the primitive associations of dominance and defeat that it triggers in the brain. Wearing it may release natural performance-enhancing drugs such as testosterone in the wearer, and reduce these in the opponent.

Red also has connotations of danger – probably because of its association with blood. In situations like shopping, it tends as a result to make people tense. As Joseph Bellizzi of Arizona State University showed, shoppers were more likely to purchase items and avoid delaying decisions to buy in a red-themed shopping area than in a blue-themed one.[12]

Red signals dominance throughout nature. Sarah Pryke at Macquarie University in Sydney studied a bird called the Gouldian Finch. Genetically, they can be either red or black-headed, and the red-headed ones almost always win contests such as who gets to the bird feeder first. Pryke took young finches whose heads were not yet coloured and put a red head mask on half of them: this simple transformation turned them into aggressive and dominant winners.[13]

And Sara Khan and her colleagues from Dartmouth College in New Hampshire discovered something similar with wild macaque monkeys in Puerto Rico. They looked at how likely these monkeys were to steal food from a researcher wearing a red T-shirt and baseball cap versus one wearing a green or blue outfit and found that the monkeys were very much less likely to approach the researcher wearing red to steal some apple.[14]

This brings us a little closer to solving the cichlid fish mystery. But the NT cichlid fish which mysteriously changed into the lavishly coloured T fish were not painted in their dominant hues by some benevolent lake god. So what happened to them? To get somewhat closer to the bottom of the mystery we have to ask another question about a strange meeting between the American and Soviet presidents that happened just after the fall of the Berlin Wall.

Home sweet home

It was 2 December 1989, and Laurie Firestone, White House Social Secretary, had organised a lavish banquet for the historic summit between President George H.W. Bush of the USA and President

Mikhail Gorbachev of the Soviet Union. But suddenly the news came in: Gorbachev would not be coming. The banquet was cancelled, as Firestone describes in her book *An Affair to Remember: State Dinners for Home Entertaining*. What had happened?

In the weeks leading up to the summit, the world watched with bated breath as the Soviet Empire disintegrated. Eastern European communist dictatorships tumbled one by one into a political turmoil unseen since the Second World War. It was critical for the Soviet Union's 'Perestroika' reform programme that President Gorbachev meet with President Bush, in order to forge a new world order and guard against the dangers that might arise out of such major instability.

But in spite of the looming emergency, the arrangements for the meeting kept stalling. Was it some key political or military agenda item that was responsible? Perhaps one or both of the leaders had dissenting advisers who kept sabotaging the meeting? Did Gorbachev fear an assassination attempt?

No. The reason for the delays was much more prosaic: the two sides couldn't agree *where* to meet. The old political order was falling apart. Volatile dictatorships were disintegrating, leaving bunkers bristling with nuclear missiles under uncertain political control. Chaos was looming, the risk enormous. Yet Mikhail and George could not decide where to meet.

The entire world was at their disposal. It was mid-winter, and they could have chosen any sun-warmed beach or birdsong-filled glade on the planet, where they would plan the safety of the world and escape the raw, biting cold of Washington and Moscow. So where did they finally choose for this cold December meeting? On two ships anchored in the bilious winter swell of a slate-grey Mediterranean in Marsaxlokk Bay, Malta.

The sailors of the USS *Belknap* were loosed on Laurie Firestone's banquet as Mikhail Gorbachev sat miserable and seasick on the

Soviet liner *Maxim Gorky:* he had been too frightened of the twenty-foot waves from the easterly storm to brave the bouncing ride in a small launch to the *Belknap*. President Bush and his staff quickly decided that they had to go to Gorbachev if he was too fearful to come to them as planned, and they made very sure that news photographers captured the fearless and virile US president standing bare-headed, braced against the gale, speeding instead across the sea to meet the seasick Gorbachev on his ship.[15]

During what became known as the 'seasick summit', the leaders engaged in discussions that ranged from Afghanistan to Europe. It is widely accepted that it was at this meeting that the end of the Cold War was effectively declared. But why on earth did they choose to meet on two rocking ships in winter waters?

The California mouse helps explain this. As Matthew Fuxjager's research showed earlier, winning only changes the mouse's brain when he wins at home. The staff of Bush and Gorbachev didn't know about mice, but, like Don King and the boxing promoters, they knew about winning. In fact, one possibility is that both politicos had learned from sport about the power of the home field advantage. This advantage happens in most sports. In soccer, Nick Neave and Sandy Wolfson of Northumbria University in England discovered that players had higher levels of testosterone in their saliva before a home game than before an away game, and for important matches against big rivals, the testosterone levels were particularly high.[16]

Playing at home, then, gives players from in many sports the sort of advantage that the California mouse enjoys when he wins a home match: remember, when that happens, his brain sprouts new receptors that boost his will to win and make him more likely to beat his opponent the next time he fights. It seems that something similar may happen when humans challenge one another on the sport field.

This explains why some games 'take off'. If both teams see the other as a major rival, then the brain motivation circuits will be ramped up and players will give their all. And some teams will have more of a home advantage than others: in European soccer, for instance, Balkan countries such as Serbia have a much higher home-advantage record than northern European countries.[17] It may be that some teams and countries are more 'pumped up' by their home territory – possibly because of high levels of nationalism – and that their brains are changed more significantly by home victories, leading to a bigger home-based winner effect in general.

This makes some sort of sense for sport – but does it really apply to portly diplomats and ageing presidents meeting to discuss global politics? It seems that it may.

Graham Brown of the University of British Columbia and Markus Baer of Washington University watched business students as they carried out a very realistic negotiation exercise where they had to get the best price for wholesale coffee for a large hotel chain, either as buyer or seller.[18] Students negotiated in their 'home' office, or in a neutral one, or in the 'away' office of their negotiating counterpart.

The results were startling: no matter whether they were buyer or seller, the negotiators who were on 'home ground' struck better deals – lower prices as buyers and higher prices as sellers – than those who were on neutral or 'away' territory.

Other people have shown this home field advantage in political negotiations. Stalin's success in having the crucial territory-allocating negotiations at the end of the Second World War located on Soviet territory in Potsdam, Germany, for instance, may have been crucial in post-war history, one scholar argued.[19]

Throughout history, neutral venues rightly have been seen as critical to avoid the home field advantage. So, for instance on 7 July
1807, two emperors – Napoleon of France and Tsar Alexander I
of Russia – ended a bloody war by meeting and signing a peace
treaty known as the Treaty of Tilsit on a raft in the middle of the
Neman river, which formed the border between their empires.

So, as President Bush clambered up the greasy, bucking gang-
plank of the *Maxim Gorky* and Laurie Firestone brooded over
the sailor-discarded slops of her sparkling banquet, neither of
the negotiating teams' brains had the home field advantage.
Who knows, perhaps this may have been a factor in the summit's
success? True, Bush was on a Russian liner, but, for Gorbachev,
the likely humiliation of having backed out of the agreed journey to the USS *Belknap* would have more than outweighed any
testosterone dribble that a weak home-ship advantage would
have conferred.

So are we getting closer to solving the cichlid fish mystery?
Has his mysterious transformation something to do with the
home advantage? Before answering that, let's consider some
more of this business of winning and its effects on people. What
is going on in people's minds to explain the winner effect?

Do you remember the game Rock, Paper, Scissors? Try this. First,
hold your hand in the scissors position and keep it there while
you answer some questions of yourself. Ask yourself whether
each of these descriptions applies to you on a 1–5 scale (1 = not
at all, 5 = very much so).

Do you consider yourself to be:

a) assertive?
b) persistent?
c) hesitating?

d) fearful?
e) esteemed?
f) respected?
g) aggrieved?
h) insulted?

Now change your hand position to the rock position and hold it there while you answer the questions again:

Do you consider yourself to be:

a) assertive?
b) persistent?
c) hesitating?
d) fearful?
e) esteemed?
f) respected?
g) aggrieved?
h) insulted?

Was there a difference in your ratings? This is meant to be done with a group of people, with half rating themselves holding the scissors position and half holding the rock position, so you, an individual, may well not have noticed any difference. But when Thomas Schubert and Sander Koole of the Free University in Amsterdam tried this with groups of men randomly allocated to either rock or scissors postures, they discovered that men making a fist felt more assertive and esteemed than men making the scissors.[20] What is going on here?

Before I explain, try another exercise. Take a pencil and hold it between your teeth, with your lips open. Now hold it between your closed lips. If you ask hundreds of people to rate their mood while holding the pencil in either of these two positions, you will find a small but statistically significant better mood in the teeth than in the lips condition. And the explanation for this is similar to that for the rock-scissors finding.

The mind, brain and body are all intimately linked. Take a moment to imagine yourself picking up a heavy suitcase – close your eyes, feel yourself bracing against its weight. As you do this, almost all the same parts of the brain kick into action as if you really were lifting a bag. What's more, the muscles of your body will show tiny movements as you imagine doing this – in other words, your body helps you imagine and think about lifting the bag.

But it works the other way too: our thoughts and emotions are triggered by the bodily expressions that normally accompany them. When I feel sad, my mouth curls down – so when I artificially curl my mouth by holding a pencil between my lips, I create a little bit of sadness in my mind. Artificially curl up my lips by holding a pencil between my teeth, and I ignite a little bit of happiness, as well as happiness's corresponding activity in my brain.

And so to the fist: in men, making a fist is associated with the threat and dominance of primitive physical rivalry, which is much more common in boys than girls. Whether this is for cultural or biological reasons doesn't matter: in men, making a fist is associated with assertion and dominance. In women it is not, and I'll come back to this in Chapter 5.

If we watched a video of the Brazilian fans during the World Cup Final, we would see many clenched fists raised in triumph. Watch any demonstration or victory rally across the world and we see the same: this is the universal signal of victory, and *power*. This is why speakers at a rally will try to rouse the audience to clench-fisted shouts of triumph: the very act of doing this will increase their sense of individual power and so boost the confidence in their mass action, whether political, industrial or social.

When Brazil beat Italy in that World Cup Final, that was a real event with real positive psychological consequences for the fans, and tangible economic benefits to their country. The boost in testosterone that they showed is maybe not too surprising in the face of such an important victory.

These apparently trivial psychological experiments involving making a fist and then asking people to rate themselves might not seem relevant to real life. Before I show that they are, first let's take another quick glance into the real world of international diplomacy.

On 22 October 2007, French President Nicolas Sarkozy met King Mohammed VI of Morocco at the Royal Palace in Marrakesh to take part in the signing ceremony for a trade agreement. Sitting beside his host, Sarkozy relaxed back into his chair and crossed one leg over the other. There was a sharp intake of breath among the watching officials as they saw the sole of Sarkozy's shoe pointing at the King. Showing the sole of one's shoe is an insult in the Islamic world, and pointing it at the King was unforgivable. But though the economic power of France may have led the Moroccans to forgive this cultural gaffe, the US Ambassador to Morocco, writing in a leaked memo to the State Department in Washington, noted that there was 'much gossip in Moroccan salons about a "too relaxed" president slouching comfortably in his chair'.[21]

President Sarkozy's cross-legged 'slouch' was not only relaxed – it was *expansive* – it literally took up space. This is a classic characteristic of a dominant human – or any dominant creature for that matter. Alpha types – like the male peacock fanning his tail or the gorilla swelling his chest – physically expand themselves in a display of dominance that asserts their status.

This is exactly what President Sarkozy was doing. Yes, he was relaxed, but this was because he felt dominant and in control, and his expansive, somewhat disrespectful posture mirrored his top-dog feelings. As I'll show later in the book, this type of dominant power helps unwind us by turning down the level of the crucial stress hormone cortisol, which is part of an emergency response system the body uses to deal with danger or threat. It does so in part by pumping glucose into the blood and brain, and in the short term cortisol is a useful get-out-of-trouble substance, but high levels over the long term can have bad consequences for the body, as we shall see in the next two chapters.

One would guess that the various ambassadors and function-aries surrounding the King and the President may have been making themselves physically small – arms folded, legs tight together, heads slightly bowed, shoulders hunched, and so on. In the presence of powerful leaders, that is what we all tend to do. It shows we know our place in the pecking order.

This is apparent in any business meeting. The most senior person at the table will be the one most likely to stretch back in his chair, clasp his hands behind his head, stick out his elbows and stretch out his legs. Alternatively, and more alarmingly for the juniors in the room, he might hunch forward over the table, head thrust out, hands clasped well out into the neutral no man's land of the table. The wary juniors, meanwhile, will be reducing their space as much as possible, just like the diplomats surround-ing President Sarkozy.

Is this not just a feature of the strange world of power poli-tics? Surely it has nothing to do with everyday life? Oh yes, it has. In the fist experiment that you did earlier, the idea was that the trappings of dominance – the clenched fist – could actu-ally make you feel more powerful because of the learned links between the feelings and their bodily expression. But what about the type of expansive slouch that Nicolas Sarkozy engaged in? Would this also boost feelings of power?

Dana Carney and her colleagues from Columbia and Harvard Universities put this question to the test by asking volunteers to strike poses for one minute at a time which were either Sarkozy-type expansive power poses, or junior diplomat-type contracted poses.[22] An expansive, 'high power' pose would be leaning back on a chair with feet on the table, and the explanation given to the participants was that the researchers needed to have the legs raised above the heart so as to get proper physiological recordings. A contracted 'low power' pose would be, for instance, standing with head slightly bowed and arms folded tightly across the chest.

Even though they held these positions for only one minute at a time, the groups who took the high power poses rated themselves as significantly more 'in charge' and 'powerful' than those who took the low power poses.

This could seem like a pretty trivial finding – a minute of standing in a particular position makes both men and women rate themselves as feeling more 'in charge'. Except that the couple of minutes in the posture also changes something else, something that we saw is key to the winner effect – testosterone. Among the twenty-six women and sixteen men who took part, those who struck the brief high power poses showed significant increases in testosterone to match their increased 'I feel in charge' feelings, while those in the low power poses showed an equivalent decrease in testosterone which was in line with their lowered 'in charge' feelings.

But there was another important hormonal change triggered by the poses struck: levels of the stress hormone cortisol decreased after the high power poses and increased after the low power poses. No wonder Sarkozy looked so relaxed – the sense of power and control he felt boosted his testosterone and soothed his nerves by turning down the anxiety-linked hormone cortisol.

The lessons of this for all strands of life, from family to business, are pretty considerable. Even tiny, short-lasting changes in the way we hold ourselves can change our bodies and brains in profound ways. No wonder parents urge their adolescents not to slump. Of course Sandhurst and West Point drill sergeants spend months building a broad-chested, erect posture in their officer cadets. Naturally trade union leaders raise their fists in assertions of victory at mass meetings.

The lesson is clear: no matter what I feel inside, if I *behave as if* I feel the way I want to feel, the feelings will likely follow. Then I might enter a positive feedback loop, where other people respond to me in such a way as to confirm or support these initially faked emotions.

If we behave like we are winners, then does that make us winners? Is there something making the NT cichlid fish *behave* differently, thus triggering the dramatic changes in his body? But what about the existing T cichlid fish – how do they tolerate this new-found dominance in the NT fish they used to bully? We are getting close to solving the NT cichlid fish mystery, but this question of how others react to us has to be addressed before we finally nail the answer.

In 1954, civil servant Anne Feeney handed in her letter of resignation to the head of her department in Dublin, Ireland. A clever, ambitious woman, she did not want to resign, but, by law, she had to. Why? Because she was about to get married. Until 1973, women civil servants in Ireland were not allowed to work unless they remained single.

On 5 August 1962, in the early hours of a fragrant African spring, a gang of policemen, tipped off by the US Central Intelligence Agency, burst into a house and seized a man, dragging him into custody from which he would not emerge until twenty-seven years later. That man was Nelson Mandela.

Both of these cases show how adept the human race is at depriving people of the chance of winning in life. All around the world, groups of people, identified by race, gender, politics or religion, are systematically stripped of their chance to exercise power over their own lives and to be successful.

When we consider the mystery of the cichlid fish, the question arises of whether there is some biological explanation for the prejudice and discrimination that subjugates millions of people. Were the T cichlid fish acting like an Afrikaaner elite in systematically oppressing the NT cichlid fish? Were they behaving like a conspiracy of male elders banning women from work, education or even public places in order to preserve their own power?

Glass ceilings as crude as those against women in 1950s Ireland or against blacks in Apartheid-era South Africa have been removed by equality legislation, civil disobedience or other social movements. But they are still prevalent, even in enlightened countries with strong norms and legal safeguards against discrimination. Take a look at a 2009 survey of the CEOs of the Fortune 500 companies – fifteen out of 500 were women.[23] This looks like clear evidence of men actively discriminating against women and obstructing their paths towards success in the workplace. But maybe it's not quite as simple as that.

Barack Obama, brain surgeon

It is May 2008 and Barack Obama and Hillary Clinton are slugging it out in a series of primaries for the Democratic nomination for the November 2008 presidential election. While this was happening, E. Ashby Plant and colleagues from Florida State University discovered a quite remarkable change happening in the brains of a sample of US citizens.[24]

To explain these changes we need to make a brief excursion into attitudes to gender, and in particular how these are measured. If I want to know your attitudes towards, say, affirmative action to increase the number of women in senior academic positions, then I ask you to say how much you support this, on a scale from 'very much' to 'not at all'. But this common-sense method taps into only one part of your mind, that of so-called *explicit*, conscious attitudes. But these are only a small fraction of the mental processes going on across the web of brain connections inside our skulls.

Most of what is going on in the brain is unconscious. And what we say, do and feel at any moment is strongly shaped by these unconscious – also known as *implicit* – processes. Frequently, these conscious and unconscious systems can drive us to behave in quite contradictory ways, and this is one reason why human behaviour often appears to be erratic and whimsically irrational.

But how do we study thoughts and feelings that are invisible even to the people having them? Quite simply, in fact, by using a method called the Implicit Association Test (IAT). A typical version of the IAT was used in 2001 by Laurie Rudman and colleagues at Rutgers University.[25] They studied implicit or unconscious attitudes to gender in the following way: words flashed up on the computer screen, and participants pressed a left key or a right key on the computer keyboard. The first set was a list of male and female names, and they had to press the left button if the name was male, and right if the name was female. Next they had to decide whether a new set of words appearing were powerful (e.g., 'strong', 'bold') or weak (e.g., 'vulnerable', 'timid') adjectives, pressing one of the two keys to signal which each adjective was.

But then came the test – names and adjectives were mixed up, appearing one by one, and they had to press the left key for both female names and weak adjectives, and the right key for male names and powerful adjectives. Then, in a second run of the test, they had to press the left key for female names and powerful adjectives, and the right key for male names and weak adjectives – in other words the same response was now required for two uneasy bedfellows – female and powerful in one case, and male and weak in the other.

The critical measure here was how fast they responded to the words: the test progressed too quickly, and there were too many decisions to be made, for the participants to be aware of the clashing stereotypes in such a way as to consciously change their responses. How fast they reacted to the words reflects implicit, unconscious, associations embedded in their brains.

Here is the crucial comparison in this study: it was between how fast people responded when each response was *compatible* with the stereotype (e.g., left key for both male and powerful) and how fast they responded when each response was *incompatible* with the stereotype (e.g., right key for both female and powerful). What Rudman found was that both men's and women's reaction times were slower when the same hand was responding to female/powerful and male/weak than when it was reacting to female/weak and male/powerful (though men showed the effect more strongly than women). In this case, that difference in reaction times is a measure of the brain's hidden attitudes to gender, but the same principle can be used for any other attitudes, whether to environmental issues, morality, politics, race – or indeed affirmative action for women, as in Plant's election-year study.

Having asked for *conscious* opinions about the issue of women in senior university positions, Plant could use the IAT method to probe *unconscious* attitudes. For instance, to go back to the affirmative action in favour of senior academic positions for women, a participant might be asked to press one button for both women's names and senior academic job titles (e.g., 'full professor'), and the other for men's names and junior job titles (e.g., 'assistant professor'). If your reaction times were slower for the women-senior button than for a women-junior button, then this would give an insight into your unconscious, implicit attitudes to the promotion of women.

So while a liberal-minded person may say, quite honestly, that he 'strongly supports' affirmative action policies for women in universities, his unconscious attitudes to women in senior positions may be negative – and he won't have a clue that this is the case. What's more, when it comes to what we actually *do* – to our *behaviour* – often it is the unconscious, implicit attitudes that really drive us.

Plant and his colleagues used methods similar to the IAT one used in gender attitudes research, to study the implicit racial attitudes of non-black people in the context of Barack Obama's campaign for the Democratic Party presidential candidacy. They were puzzled to find significantly lower levels of unconscious prejudice against black people during the Democratic primaries than had previously been measured. The exposure to the positive example of a highly intelligent and effective black person in a pre-eminent position – Barack Obama – seems to have reshaped the unconscious attitudes embedded invisibly in the tissue of people's brains.

That we are really talking about physical changes in the brain underpinning these attitudes is shown by research by Elizabeth Phelps and her colleagues from New York University, who showed pictures of black and white strangers to white people whose degree of racial prejudice they had measured in two ways – by giving them a standard attitudes questionnaire, or using the IAT to measure their unconscious bias.[26] Phelps used fMRI brain imaging to look at activity in the amygdala – a key brain area for emotions such as fear and anger. While conscious racial prejudice measured by the questionnaire was *unrelated* to the amygdala's activity in the brain, unconscious, implicit prejudice was strongly related to the amount of amygdala activity while the participants saw black rather than white faces.

Conscious thought is slow and has a very narrow bottleneck, meaning that it is very hard to follow more than one train of thought at a time. Unconscious thought, on the other hand, is very fast and does not have the same bottleneck. For this simple reason, most of the time in the business of everyday life, what we do and say is much more controlled by implicit, unconscious processes than it is by conscious ones. This makes it less surprising that how we *think* we feel about politics, gender, race and other similar matters does not map well on to the activity in the parts of the brain that really count when it comes to predicting how we will behave in a given situation. Our IAT performance, in other words, is probably a more accurate measure of what we *really* prefer than is what we consciously think and say to ourselves and other people.

You can probe your own unconscious bias using IAT-type tests, then you can get a readout of them by doing the tests at this Harvard website: https://implicit.harvard.edu/implicit/. I took part in an experiment on this website which measured implicit attitudes to different age groups using an IAT method similar to the ones I described earlier. By measuring my reaction times I came out as unconsciously most positively disposed towards children and middle-aged adults, followed closely by old adults, with my unconscious attitude to young adults falling significantly below the other groups – which, as a university professor, made me sit up and think.

But conscious bias and prejudice is pretty universal too, and there was nothing implicit or unconscious in the discrimination that Anne Feeney and Nelson Mandela experienced. But where prejudice is conscious it can be recognised and combated. Much more difficult to deal with are the unconscious attitudes concealed in the brains of even liberal-minded people who honestly voice non-prejudiced attitudes. A combination of explicit and implicit prejudice in the minds of the truly prejudiced constitutes one of the most formidable barriers to winning and empowerment in discriminated-against groups. The particular problem with the implicit prejudices is that, unless we allow our unconscious to be probed by an IAT-type test, we may not even know that we are prejudiced, in spite of the fact that our unconscious attitudes actually shape how we behave in the real world.

There is, however, an even more insidious barrier against winning – one that is inside the brain of the discriminated-against person.

Glass ceilings of the brain

On 28 March 1964, twenty-nine-year-old Barbara Allen sat down at the lunch counter of a diner in St Augustine, Florida. Minutes later a group of policemen burst in and ordered her to leave. When she didn't, electric cattle prods were applied to her body, causing a muscle spasm that slammed her knee against the counter. The policemen arrested her and dragged her out[27].

Barbara had travelled to Florida from New York to take her place in the civil rights movement, which, due to vehement local opposition from the Ku Klux Klan and St Augustine police and judicial functionaries, had reached a malignant low point in St Augustine, the continental USA's oldest European-founded city. Afterwards, Barbara, who was black, lost her job in the post office because of the resulting criminal record, and was denied the chance to go to college to train as a nurse.

Barbara Allen's sacrifice, along with those of thousands of others, led to the 1964 Civil Rights Act being enacted in Washington. And as protesters were being beaten, savaged by dogs and occasionally killed in the southern states, meanwhile in liberal New York University, Irwin Katz and his team in the Research Center on Human Relations were beginning to study racial prejudice. The title of their first study may make modern eyes water a little: 'Effects of task difficulty, race of administrator, and instructions on digit-symbol performance of Negroes', published in the respected *Journal of Personality and Social Psychology*.[28]

Katz and his team travelled down to the tense and violent south, where they gave black students a test that is a subtest of the Wechsler Adult Intelligence Scale (the international gold-standard measure of IQ) – the 'digit symbol' test. Doing this involves matching abstract symbols to numbers in a fixed time against a stopwatch held by the tester. Half the testers were white and half were black. And, crucially, the researchers told some students that it was a test of eye-hand co-ordination and others that it was a test of intelligence.

The results were remarkable: students tested by a black person performed very slightly better when told that it was an intelligence test than when told it was an eye–hand co-ordination measure. But when examined by a white tester, their performance dropped like a stone – but *only when* they thought it was an intelligence test; they performed much better when they believed that exactly the same test measured 'eye–hand co-ordination'.

Why was this such a remarkable piece of research? Because, for the first time, it showed how prejudice could embed itself into the brains of the victims of prejudice. This malignant implant created self-fulfilling prophecies: because black people were believed by many to be less intelligent than whites, this false stereotype burrowed unconsciously into the minds of black people and made their scores on tests of intellectual ability lower than they otherwise should have been.

These glass ceilings of the brain constitute an incredibly powerful blockage to winning – in many ways much harder to combat than the overt discrimination that Barbara Allen fought against. How do you fight against something that is inside your own head, and, what's more, is *unconscious*? Furthermore, this is not just a problem for black people – it is equally a challenge for other stereotyped and discriminated-against groups. Take gender, for instance, where there is a stereotype that women are less good at mathematics than men. If women are given numerical problems but are told that these are 'not diagnostic of mathematical ability', they will do much better than if the very same problems are described as 'indicators of mathematical ability'.[29]

These internalised glass ceilings apply to stereotypes about age as well. Consider this remarkable finding by John Bargh and his colleagues at New York University.[30] Students were given five cards, with one word on each – a set like *ran fork dog the home*, for instance. Their job was to make a four-word sentence out of the five words – *the dog ran home*. They were tested on thirty such sets and sent away, believing the study had ended. But there was a catch . . .

Unbeknown to the participants – either before or after – for some of the people, slipped into twenty of their thirty sets was a word linked to the negative aspects of ageing – words like *old*, *lonely*, *grey*, *forgetful*, *retired*, etc. The other participants, again quite unbeknown to them, saw only neutral words not linked to ageing.

So here is the astonishing finding: as they left the room, believing they had finished the study, a student researcher sat unobtrusively in the corridor and timed their walking speed as they walked along it. What happened? The students who had been unconsciously, implicitly exposed to the age-related words *walked significantly slower*.

In other words, Bargh and his colleagues had built a glass ceiling into their students' brains – they were unconsciously 'programmed' into behaving according to the stereotype of an old person, one feature of which is walking slowly. They had *no awareness* of what had made them do this – in fact, they were not even aware that they were walking any differently from usual!

But what about that other bugbear of growing old – *memory*? Surely that is only a feature of immutable biological processes in the brain and cannot be affected by apparently trivial manipulations of the unconscious mind? Not so. Thomas Hess and his colleagues at North Carolina State University used John Bargh's mental glass ceiling method with groups of young and old people as they did memory tests.[31] They used the same word-sorting puzzles, but changed them a little.

For half of the young and half of the old volunteers, Hess slipped negative words linked to ageing into twenty of their thirty lists – words like *brittle, complaining, confused, cranky, dependent, depressed, feeble, forgot, fragile, grumpy, incompetent, inflexible, lonely, rigid, sedentary, senile, sickly, slowly, stubborn, tired*. The other participants, again quite unbeknown to them, had seen *positive* words linked to ageing among their problems, words like *accomplished, active, alert, dignified, distinguished, experience, generous, independence, insightful, interesting, kindness, knowledgeable, loving, patience, pride, respected, sociable, successful, understanding, wise.*

So, with half of the people 'glass-ceilinged' by the unconsciously implanted negative ageing words, Hess then gave them all a memory test – they had to remember a list of new words. Not surprisingly, the younger people, who ranged in age from nineteen to thirty, remembered more of the words than the older people, aged from sixty-two to eighty-four; what's more, the glass ceiling didn't work with the young people – their memory wasn't affected by either the positive or negative ageing words.

But it was a different story for the older group: unconsciously primed with the positive ageing words, they remembered 53 per cent of the words, against the younger group's 62 per cent. When their negative stereotypes about age were unconsciously primed, however, their retention of the words dropped to 40 per cent.

Hess and his colleagues also discovered something else. They noticed that some of the older people were less vulnerable to worsened memory with the negative stereotype. Who were they? They were the ones whose implicit, unconscious attitudes to ageing were less negative. In other words, the implicit glass ceiling of the brain may have been the crucial factor in depressing their memories in response to the negative ageing words.[32]

Memory can be dragged down by a tiny probe to their unconscious – as IQ can in black people and mathematical ability in women, as shown in the other studies. All stigmatised groups' chances of winning in life are sabotaged by the insertion of stereotypes into their brains, which create unconscious, self-imposed glass ceilings that further create self-fulfilling prophecies in their performance. In other words, not only are they cut off from the opportunity to be 'T-fished' by the attitudes and beliefs of other people, they also shackle themselves by unconsciously adopting the very same negative attitudes.

Could Barack Obama's election to president, therefore, conceivably be one of the biggest mass neurological interventions in US history? We saw from Ashby Plant's research that the positive achievements of Obama seemed to reshape the unconscious brain processes of the general public, but could it also have removed some glass ceilings from the brains of black people? Does that illustrate a possible, though less extreme, human equivalent of the sort of loser-to-winner transformation that the NT-to-T cichlid fish showed?

The mystery of the cichlid fish solved

There are, so far as we know, no glass ceilings in the brains of NT cichlid fish. Nor are T cichlid fish capable of the sorts of organised oppression that the Saint Augustine police applied to Barbara Allen. So what happens to trigger the bizarre transformation of the NT cichlid fish to its strutting, dominant T cichlid self?

Here is the answer: the gorgeous colouring that comes with the transformation makes them stand out from the crowd of NT cichlid fish. And while that is good when it comes to interesting the cichlid females, it has one major downside – the birds circling hungrily above can see them more easily. So T cichlid fish are at higher risk of being eaten. And when this happens, a nearby opportunistic NT cichlid fish may be lucky enough to grab the swallowed T cichlid fish's territory before anyone else can.

And when that happens, the simple experience of having territory is the stimulus that triggers the incredible transformation of the male cichlid fish from its NT to its T version. Their transformation to beautiful, dominant winner was as a result in the opportunity afforded by a change in environment.

Is there something to this when it comes to human behaviour? Is winning simply a feature of the luck of the draw – a simple matter of being lucky enough to inherit the territory, real or metaphorical? Does simply being made the lord of the manor, or the boss of the department, or the student in the high-status school turn us, Jekyll and Hyde-like, into T cichlid fish? Is it simply a question of 'Cometh the hour, cometh the man?' Is our success, then, made by the roles we are assigned, the power that others give us?

Do winning qualities – the judgement, the charisma, the decisiveness – of famous CEOs like Jack Welch of General Electric or Ursula M. Burns of Xerox – arise out of the roles people find themselves in? Does becoming a president create new abilities and qualities that allow the incumbent to perform at much higher levels than would otherwise be the case? Is it like Odlanier Solís being given the red shirt to wear and so, against the odds, winning the Olympic gold medal? Can we, in other words, be transformed like the NT cichlid fish by chance, circumstance or business 'territory' into the corporate equivalents of the T cichlid fish?

If this is the case, then it may explain how countries, families and businesses can waste an enormous amount of human potential because their workers are deprived of their T fish capacities by the limitations imposed on them, consciously and unconsciously, by the actual and glass ceilings around them. How does one metaphorically give the NT cichlid fish in our families, schools, communities, and organisations the chance to become T cichlid fish?

With winning and power 'made' by others, and by our own unconscious attitudes, success seems simply a matter of being given the opportunities and the expectations to behave like a winner. This explanation has more traction than the 'born to win' theory of the previous chapter, but there is still a problem: as we all know, giving someone status does not guarantee that they will live up to it. How many 'excellent number two' people spring to mind – individuals who make superb deputies and seem the obvious choice to replace the retiring boss, but who when they become the top dog often flop spectacularly, in spite of being given the T cichlid fish territory?

No, winning is not just a matter of chance or circumstance – we are not simply pawns of circumstance any more than we are born inevitably to win. So if success is not an inevitable outcrop of our birthright, and if it is not just chance and circumstance that make winners or losers of us, what additional ingredients are needed?

To answer that question, we have to explore the question of power some more. What happens to human beings when they are given the sort of power that the T cichlid fish gets as a result of getting lucky in the lake real estate? Power, if we are to believe the British philosopher Bertrand Russell, is the fundamental *stuff* of human relationships, but more than just changing relationships, does it also transform people? Is there some sort of chemistry between the cards that chance deals you on the one hand, and your personality on the other?

Let us now turn to the question of what power might *do* to us – by tackling the enigma of Bill Clinton's friend.

The Enigma of Bill Clinton's Friend

What does power do to us?

On 28 May 1997, President Bill Clinton and his wife Hillary ate dinner with a friend and his wife at one of London's top restaurants, the Pont de La Tour, overlooking Tower Bridge. All smart, high-powered lawyers, they got on well and the occasion probably helped distract a newly re-elected President beset by domestic political woes. His party had lost control over both Congress and Senate, his health reforms had crashed and burned and a number of other very large political sharks were circling below him.

Days before, Bill Clinton's friend had swept to power in a landslide British election and it was a marker of the strength of their relationship that the US president should pay him such an early and high-profile visit. The boyish Tony Blair may have reminded Clinton of himself five years earlier, Clinton's staff had mentored Blair to his landslide victory and the two also shared a political vision known as the 'third way'.

It was only a year later when one of the sharks – the Monica Lewinsky affair – broke surface, on the eve of a Blair visit to Washington. At President Clinton's lowest ebb, Blair gave a moving speech at the White House in support of his friend that gave him some much-needed political capital. Yet a year later, Bill Clinton was accusing Tony Blair of having stabbed him in the back. What happened? The answer to this question will help us to understand how and why becoming a winner can depend on how you respond to power.

TV news channels showed in March 1999 images of vast straggling columns of women, children and old men driven from their homes in Kosovo by the ethnic cleansing of Slobodan Milosevic, then president of Yugoslavia. The US and its European allies in NATO had given him an ultimatum to cease his assault or be bombed – but among the allies there was disagreement as to whether ground troops would ultimately be needed to bring Milosevic to heel.

On 24 March, Bill Clinton made a prime-time statement declaring that US planes had joined with NATO allies in attacking Serbian forces. At the last minute before the broadcast, according to David Halberstam, in his book *War in a Time of Peace: Bush, Clinton and the Generals*, the President had inserted the sentence 'I do not intend to put our troops in Kosovo to fight a war' into his statement.[1]

Back in London, his friend Blair was furious, believing that excluding the ground troops option essentially neutered the military campaign and played into Milosevic's hands. A month later, Blair gave a speech in Chicago in which he said, 'We will not have succeeded until an international force has entered Kosovo and allowed the refugees to return to their homes. Milosevic will have no veto on the entry of this international force.'

It was a rousing, hard-line speech advocating pre-emptive action across international borders. He went on to say, 'If anything Americans are too ready to see no need to get involved in affairs of the rest of the world,' and then expressed confidence that that weekend's conference in Washington led by President Clinton would show a unified resolve for the actions Blair was advocating.

Clinton's anger at Blair's upstaging of him was understandable: the US public's response to Blair was positive. His combative, moralistic tone painted him in a very favourable light compared with a Bill Clinton weakened by allegations of draft dodging during the Vietnam War and sexual impropriety.

So perhaps it is not much of a mystery – the friendship split up because of a betrayal of the friendship by Tony Blair. But that begs the question, how did these relationship-straining differences between President Clinton and Prime Minister Blair arise? Were they simply a feature of political differences, or could some other more psychological factor have come into play?

On 3 October 1993, two US helicopters were shot down, and three others damaged, by rocket-propelled grenades in Mogadishu, Somalia. They were part of a US-led multinational force which, sanctioned by the United Nations, had entered Somalia in order to create a protected environment within which humanitarian operations could take place in this failing state riven by conflict between the armies of many different warlords. Predictably, the force came under attack and in the helicopter crash and subsequent ground-troop action, eighteen US servicemen were killed and seventy-four injured, along with hundreds of Somalis.[2] The images of the downed Black Hawk helicopters and of the corpse of a US serviceman being dragged through the streets shocked the nation, and Clinton's newly hatched presidency suffered badly as he quickly ordered US troops to leave Somalia within six months.

Just a week after the Somalia disaster, the USS *Harlan County* with 200 US soldiers on board was not allowed to dock in Port au Prince, Haiti, where it had planned to help reinstate the elected President Aristide, who had been deposed in a coup. As crowds jeered 'Somalia, Somalia' from the jetty, the vessel sailed back to the USA, in what Halberstam describes as one of the most embarrassing episodes in America's recent history.

By the time the crisis in Kosovo had come to a head in 1999, and Blair give his famous Chicago speech, Clinton had already suffered not only the humiliations of Somalia and Haiti, but his health-care reforms had also failed, he had lost control over Congress and Senate, and he was being criticised for not having done anything to stop the horrors of the genocide in Rwanda. Now he was faced with pressure to intervene in another very complex and uncertain crisis, in Kosovo, with all the risks that that involved to him and to his troops.

Tony Blair, on the other hand, had achieved the apparently impossible task of helping to bring about a settlement of a 400-year-old conflict in Northern Ireland – albeit with the active assistance of Bill Clinton and Bertie Ahern – and major constitutional reform in the UK, among many other accomplishments.

So was it any surprise that Clinton was reluctant to commit troops to Kosovo in the light of the defeats he had suffered? Could it be that the rift in his friendship with Blair was a by-product of the 'winner effect'? Was Blair the equivalent of the mouse which has won a couple of bouts and as a result is now able to beat a more formidable opponent because victory has empowered him physically and mentally? Conversely, was Clinton like the defeated mouse showing the reverse winner effect, reluctant to take the military risks that some of his cabinet were advocating? Was the breach in the two leaders' friendship an outcome of the gulf that opens between the brains of winners and losers?

Maybe, but Clinton *had* had some successes – among them a US-brokered settlement in Bosnia in 1995, a thriving economy and his own 1996 re-election. So while his early presidential setbacks may have dulled his appetite for engaging in risk, he was still the senior partner in the friendship. So if a winner-and-loser effect does not explain the breach between them, what else could be going on?

Prominent though they may be in the public eye, presidents and prime ministers do not act alone, but rather in the context of the advising, disputing, lobbying and jousting of scores of senior cabinet colleagues and advisers, and hundreds of officials. Isn't it a little naive to interpret international conflicts in terms of the individual psychologies of single leaders?

Not entirely – as we'll see later, the psychological make-up of leaders is a pretty important factor in shaping history. But yes – it is naive to think that you can ignore all the other senior politicians, military and civil servants when trying to understand how policy differences may have triggered the breach between Blair and Clinton. To find out what might have been going on with them, we need to go back to an infamous spring day in the previous decade.

26 April 1986. A horizon-wide slab of black cloud edges across the sky from the east, snuffing out the sunlight. Columns of torrential rain plummet to the ground like soft artillery fire. I am high on a mountain on a Scottish island, drenched, involuntarily inhaling and drinking the cascading eastern rain. Does caesium 137 change the shape of raindrops, I now wonder, making them heavier, softer . . . sweeter?

The fourth reactor at Chernobyl nuclear power plant blew at 01.23 on that April morning.[3] On 25 April, the plant's engineers had been carrying out a test initiated and overseen by Anatoly Dyatlov, Deputy Chief Engineer. They aimed to test Dyatlov's prediction that the reactor would have enough cooling water even if there was a complete loss of power to the electrical generator. Given that Soviet reactors were not designed to have any of the protective second layer of outer shielding that Western nuclear power stations always had, and given the temperamental nature of Soviet electrical supplies, this was not an unreasonable test.

Dyatlov had a reputation as an irritable and domineering boss, and apparently he was particularly impatient on the night in question. He himself would have been under severe pressure from his superiors – the Soviet system was highly authoritarian and hierarchical, part of the legacy of the absolutism of Tsarist Russia and partly a result of the authoritarianism of Marxism-Leninism. In this system you did what your boss told you or you suffered the consequences – disciplinary action, demotion . . . or worse.

Just as an African swamp is the ideal breeding ground for malarial mosquitoes, so a hierarchical society like Russia and the former Soviet Union provided is the perfect breeding ground for the 'mum effect'.[4] The term comes from the phrase 'keeping mum' – that is, not telling. The mum effect is a big player in nations and organisations where power is shared unequally.

Nations and cultures differ in how hierarchical they are – in other words, how steep the social hierarchy is. A scale called the 'power-distance index', devised by the Dutch social psychologist Geert Hofstede[5] measures how unequally power is shared across different social ranks. This is a figure that quantifies the extent to which less powerful people in an organisation or society accept that power is distributed unequally – in other words, it is a measure of the steepness of the pecking order as seen from below. The figure is based on questionnaire responses by people who are relatively low down in any work, social or national hierarchy.

It is widely accepted that in countries with a high power-distance index, individuals high in the hierarchy hold considerable power, while those lower in the hierarchy hold very little. The relative powerlessness of people who are low down in the pecking order of these countries may make them understandably reluctant to give their superiors bad news if they see problems in their organisation. After all, their seniors have so much power that their employees, in their powerlessness, may be punished because of the 'shoot the messenger' culture that tends to thrives in such hierarchical cultures – hence the mum effect.

Russia comes near the top of an international league table on this pecking-order index, with a near-maximum power-distance index of 93, which is beaten only by Malaysia with 104, the Philippines with 94 and Panama and Guatemala both with 95.[6] Near the bottom are New Zealand with 22, Denmark with 18 and Israel with 13. The UK and the USA are in the lower third, with scores of 35 and 40 respectively.

We can see clear traces of ancient empires wired into the social hierarchies of modern peoples. In some of the Latin countries of Europe, for instance, an acceptance of steep hierarchies can be traced back to the absolute rule of the Roman Empire and the rule of the Roman Catholic Church that succeeded it. In the countries with a political history where rulers were more accountable – the Netherlands and England, for instance – people's attitudes to power hierarchies are less tolerant of power inequality.[7]

At Chernobyl number 4 reactor on 25 April, Dyatlov's team had calculated that the inertia of the plant's huge electric turbines would produce enough electricity for the reactor's cooling water pumps to keep operating during the short period – less than a minute – that was needed to switch on the emergency diesel generators.

For various practical reasons, Dyatlov's test could not begin until after midnight – when a new team of operators less familiar with the test and its background began work without being properly brief by the outgoing team.

The outgoing technicians hadn't liked the way the plant was responding to their initial preparations and had considered several times taking action which would have prevented what happened – such as re-enabling the automatic shutdown mechanisms which they had disabled for the test. But the nature of the mum effect is that you don't get rewarded for doing something to prevent what didn't happen – after all, it mightn't have happened, right? On the contrary, in the Soviet power hierarchy, silence was almost always the safest option. If the technicians had aborted the test, very likely they would have been punished by Dyatlov for delaying it – as he would in turn have been dumped upon by his superiors, and so on up the too-steep gradient of power.

In fact, a similar type of test had been tried once before, before the reactor was commissioned into service in 1984. The test actually failed, but the Soviet leadership ruthlessly pressured the engineers to deliver a so-called 'labour victory' by delivering the station ready for service ahead of schedule. This pressure had resulted in Chernobyl's director, Viktor Bryukhanov, who says that he believed the plant was actually safe, signing a document accepting that the power station was in order so that he could satisfy his bosses' demands. In fact, he was unwittingly certifying a power station that could not keep cool if electricity failed. It was a nuclear bomb waiting to explode. But had he not signed, he and thousands of engineers and workers would have paid the price for insubordination.

And so it was that Alexander Akimov, the new chief of the night shift, and his inexperienced operator Leonid Toptunov began their shift at midnight on 26 April. Akimov was soon puzzled – there were confusing signals coming from the reactor which, because he did not know what had gone on earlier in the day, he could only interpret as dangerous instability. For reasons that will never be known, Toptunov inserted the control rods too far into the reactor, causing a near shutdown. This caused a cascade of events culminating, at 1:23:45 a.m., in a catastrophic explosion which blew the top off the reactor, spewing a vast cloud of radioactive particles high into the grim, grey slabs of cloud preparing for their journey westward. Akimov received radiation burns on 100 per cent of his body while trying to restart the cooling water supply to the reactor and died two weeks later on 11 May, and Toptunov also died from radiation sickness three days after Akimov. A cloud of the radiation that killed them then spread across Europe: a deadly legacy, perhaps, of the mum effect.

The higher you are in a steep hierarchy, the more power you have over those below you, whether psychological, financial or physical. Power pumps testosterone into the blood, which in turn – via the winner effect – further inflates your power by helping you win in future.

The flip side of this is that the lower down a steep hierarchy you find yourself, the less power you have, and so the less hormonally empowered you are to have the 'balls' to stand up to people above you: this is one reason why, historically, most revolutions have been led by upper- or middle-class people, rather than by those lowest in the pecking order. Meekness and a reluctance to question the boss by testosterone-depleted underlings can have fatal consequences in any organisation, as we saw at Chernobyl.

The mum effect was certainly not a feature of President Clinton's administration, which was riven with disagreement and rivalry among his cabinet and advisers. Clinton heard many contrary views to his decisions, and maybe listened to too many, hence his 'flip-flop' image and 'Slick Willie' nickname. Famously, during the Haiti fiasco, he voiced support for a hunger striker who was protesting against US government policy!

Tony Blair, in contrast, had managed to reshape the way the British government operated into a much less consensus-driven affair. Largely gone was the notion of cabinet government, whereby issues were discussed and decisions arrived at after vigorous debate among peers. Instead, crucial decisions largely were made by Blair's 'sofa cabinet' (a small group of his trusted personal advisers), which subsequently managed to involve Britain in an invasion of Iraq that the country overwhelmingly did not want.

One of these advisers – his Chief of Staff Jonathan Powell – has disputed this characterisation of Blair's cabinet, reporting that he and the other principal adviser – Director of Communications Alastair Campbell – were often brutally critical of Blair, fiercely arguing alternative policy approaches in a way that could not be more different from that of disempowered subordinates.[8]

The memoirs of Blair and Campbell are in accord with this view – Campbell and Powell were Blair's sparring partners – but their tone when talking about cabinet ministers suggested a sense of superiority – and even at times contempt – for these ministers who held their jobs entirely at the discretion of the Prime Minister. The tone and anecdotes of both memoirs is that Blair delegated enormous prime-ministerial power to these long-term advisers and that Campbell and Powell shared in the pattern of thinking and dictatorial inclinations of their boss.

In 2010, one minister, Clare Short, described the style of Tony Blair's cabinet meetings in the run-up to the Iraq War.[9] 'It was not a decision-making body,' she said of the cabinet. 'I don't think there was ever a substantive discussion about anything in cabinet. If you ever raised an issue with Tony Blair he would cut it off. He did that in July 2002 when I said I wanted to talk about Iraq. He said he did not want it leaking into the press.'

Cabinet meetings were, according to Short, 'little chats' rather than decision-making opportunities. She said: 'There was never a meeting ... that said: "What is the problem? What are we trying to achieve? What are our options?"' Short also testified that she was forbidden by Tony Blair to discuss a brief summary of legal advice about the legality of the Iraq War which was tabled just three days before the war began. She describes being jeered at when she expressed her concern about this, but appears to have been crushed into silence. 'If the prime minister says be quiet, there is only so much you can do,' she wrote.

Short said that the code of practice for ministers stipulated that legal advice should be circulated, but only a short summary was circulated just before the war. One senior minister, Robin Cook, resigned in protest three days before the Iraq War began. But in spite of the apparent railroading of the cabinet and breach of guidelines, no remaining ministers other than Short raised a murmur of protest, although she hadn't resigned with Cook.

It is hard to avoid the conclusion that a version of the Mum Effect was operating in the government of Tony Blair not just in the run-up to the Iraq War, but also in earlier years during the Kosovo crisis, and that a silenced, cowed and disempowered cabinet allowed Blair to do what Clinton's cabinet would not – drive forward a policy of ground troops for Kosovo.

So is this the puzzle entirely explained? Blair, a winner effect-, testosterone-fuelled leader supported by his two equally pumped-up advisers, surrounds himself with hormone-depleted ministers who acquiesce to his decision to strong Kosovo action, allowing him to outflank his weakened senior partner, Bill Clinton, with the humiliating Chicago speech of 22 April 1999?

Not fully. Let's consider again the pre-Iraq War months of 2002–3, when Blair was joining with President George W. Bush in leading the drumbeat to that war. In Blair's cabinet, not only, as Clare Short reported, did hardly anyone have the 'balls' to oppose the leader, there also seems to have been an absence of critical judgement among some highly intelligent and sophisticated people who swallowed pretty unconvincing and subsequently discredited intelligence data about the existence of Iraqi weapons of mass destruction.

The mystery of the Clinton–Blair breach, then, can be explained by policy differences which in turn happened because the steeper power hierarchy of the Blair government apparatus allowed him to take risks that Clinton's government – as David Halberstam described – was not prepared to take. But there is still something not quite clear: why did Tony Blair – who made outstanding and courageous decisions in Ireland, Sierra Leone and Kosovo earlier in his premiership – and his advisers, make the judgements that they did? Did Blair's style of government affect his *thinking* and that of his advisers? And if so, was this another factor in the breach with Clinton?

The Russian solstice

On 22 June 1812, Napoleon Bonaparte of France launched an invasion of Russia. On precisely the same date in 1941, Reichsführer Adolf Hitler's scorching blitzkrieg into the Russian steppes commenced. Each invasion was ultimately fatal for its leader, his country and millions of men, women and children. Both men were dictators who held absolute power in their empires – theirs were the ultimate hierarchies. Both had had a string of victories, often against ill-matched opponents who crumbled in the face of their masterfully organised violence. Germany, for instance, had recently crushed the armies of Poland, Norway and France and humiliated the British Expeditionary Force at Dunkirk. Napoleon and Hitler were both primed by easy victories, pumped up with testosterone and aggressively hungry for more and greater conquests.

Hitler's dizzying successes in the early days of what was planned to be a three-month campaign followed the script dictated by the winner effect: his armies plunged murderously to the heart of Russia, sweeping aside whole armies and seemingly justifying the risky – many senior German officers were too frightened to say reckless – adventure. Such was Hitler's confidence in a quick victory that whole regiments were sent east without proper winter clothing. It is estimated that, as a result, around 14,000 German soldiers had to have hands or feet amputated because of frostbite during the subsequent winter.

Hitler's invasion of Russia cost the lives of more than twenty million Russians. Of Napoleon's 600,000-strong army – the biggest in history at that time – as few as one in three may have come back. Both of the campaigns were infamously reckless: in both cases, lines of supply and of retreat were not properly planned. In Hitler's case – all the more bizarre because of Napoleon's historical precedent[10] – the situation was intensified by his contempt for his opponents, whom he regarded as sub-human objects fit only for annihilation by the master race.

Neither dictator seemed able to admit to the catastrophic errors of judgement made, and hence both were unable to contemplate pulling back even in the face of certain disaster. Both seemed to have lost the ability to make sound judgements and were blind to a reality that resulted in the deaths of millions of people. What

was going on here? Victories boost aggression, and winning
makes you more likely to win in the future. So can power skew
the judgement of some leaders? Did Tony Blair – a largely decent
and constitutional politician who bears no comparison with
Hitler and Napoleon – have his thinking distorted by the power
he accrued as a result of his repeated successes, in a way that Bill
Clinton's was not because of his experience of several failures? To
help answer that question, try this short experiment.

All you will need is a non-toxic water-soluble crayon or marker
that will wash off your skin easily.

Do this first: think of a time in the past when you have had
power over someone. By 'power' I mean having the ability to
control something that other people wanted, or being in a position to grade or judge them. For instance, anyone who has had
to give an appraisal to a junior colleague or student would have
been in this position. Spend a couple of minutes trying to relive
that experience – not just the events, but how you felt and what
you thought; write down a few lines of description.

Having written the description of when you had power, place
the marker down beside you and do the following quickly and
without reflection:

- Snap the thumb and forefinger of your right hand (left if you
  are left-handed) five times.
- Pick up the crayon and write a capital E on your own forehead.
- Now ask yourself – what way did you draw the E: Did you
  draw an E from *your* perspective, or from the perspective of
  someone *facing* you? In other words, when you wrote the E,
  were you at that moment viewing the world from *your* point
  of view, or were you drawing it from the point of view of a
  person standing opposite you?

Professor Adam Galinsky and colleagues at Northwestern University found that this depended on the extent to which feelings of *power* had been activated in the participants' minds.[11] Those who had thought about a time when they had power over someone tended to draw an E on their forehead which was correct from *their* point of view but appeared mirror-reversed from the point of view of someone standing opposite them.

People who wrote about a time when they had been under someone else's power, on the other hand, tended to draw the E so that it was correct from others' viewpoints but mirror-reversed from their own.

These temporary manipulations of power in psychology experiments are a long way from the vast power that Napoleon and Hitler held while making decisions about their armies, but what this research does show is that, when our brains are primed by even small amounts of remembered power, this changes us psychologically: power makes us more egocentric, disinclining us to take on other points of view.

If small fluctuations in power in ordinary people can make them more or less able to take on other perspectives, what are the consequences of holding infinitely greater power for years, as Napoleon and Hitler did? Very likely, holding extreme real-life power will cause a long-term corrosion of the ability to detach from one's own point of view – a potentially fatal shortcoming, as any chess player who does not learn to visualise the board from his opponent's perspective will confirm.

So this power-induced egocentricity is one possible answer as to why Hitler repeated Napoleon's same blunder on the Russian steppes. But is that enough to explain mistakes of such proportions?

The gambler's fallacy

It is the compulsive gambler's folly to believe that he can control the roll of the dice. Whether mediated by superstitious pre-bet rituals, or by a belief in luck or destiny, fortunes have been lost under the illusion that a person has personal control over events which are in reality randomly determined – like the spin of the roulette wheel.

If you want to find out whether someone you know is susceptible to this illusion, try this: offer a small amount of money if he/she can correctly predict the outcome of the roll of a die. (If you don't have a die, go for the flip of a coin.) There is only a one-in-six (or one-in-two for the coin) chance that you will lose your money, so don't worry too much. Now, offer your volunteer the choice between you throwing the die and he/she throwing it. Try it with a few other people.

Do some choose to throw the die themselves? If so, they are showing that they are victims of the illusion of control – assuming the die is not loaded, the outcome of the throw will be random and it should not matter who throws it.

Nathanael Fast and Deborah Gruenfeld of Stanford University in California found that even tiny amounts of power increases susceptibility to this illusion.[12] Some volunteers were asked to think about a time when they had power over someone, while others had to think about a time when someone else had power over them.

Fast and his colleagues then offered the participants the choice between watching the dice being thrown, and throwing it themselves. The power-primed volunteers were more likely to choose to throw the dice, showing that they somehow believed they could control the result, while the low-power individuals were more likely to leave it to the tester to throw the die.

Giving volunteers the power of acting as a manager/evaluator of other volunteers in an artificial experimental situation also boosted their sense of control over how the dice would fall, but it also meant that they were more likely to say they felt more control over political and economic events, and more often said that they planned to vote at the next national election.

It's important to remember that these were not personality differences between individuals, who were actually chosen at random for the low-power and high-power groups: just the simple manipulation of being asked to think about a time in their past when they had a little bit of power, or being given a temporary little bit of power in an experiment, was enough to make them feel more in control of the economy and more able to influence political events!

Even transient activation of ideas of power in the brain, therefore, increased people's sense of control, even when that control was illusory. Power, then, is such a fundamental motivator that even having people think about past positions of minor power, or giving them temporary power in an artificial situation, significantly changes their outlook on life. It also increased their optimism and their self-esteem.

Magnify these tiny increases in power a thousand times to get close to the amount of power that Hitler and Napoleon exercised. If trivial increases in power can shift the sense of control over events, then it is pretty clear that absolute power must enormously magnify the sense of control over events in the brains of people like these two dictators – arguably to a delusional extent.

Napoleon and Hitler, then, may have experienced a fundamental change in brain function as a consequence of the vast power they held over millions of people. Such a change has two major consequences on judgement: first, it makes people less inclined to see events from other perspectives than their own, and second, it makes them subject to the illusion that they can control events which are too vast and complex to be controllable.

To return to Bill Clinton and Tony Blair – is there any other evidence to suggest that the rift in their relationship after Blair's Chicago speech was caused by their different experiences of success and power?

There is. The distinguished political psychologist Margaret Hermann has devised a method for so-called 'at-a-distance' assessments of the personalities and motivations of leaders. She has pinpointed a number of key behaviour patterns in world leaders, and one of these relates to the belief in *control* over events.

Hermann discovered that it was possible to systematically analyse the speech and writings of leaders to extract how much they believed the country under their leadership could be a 'player' in world events and shape the course they took. Assessing President Clinton on this dimension, she discovered that, compared with other world leaders, President Clinton had an average level of belief in his ability to shape world events.[13] For the most powerful nation on earth, this was probably a little modest, but given the complexity of the international system, and the law of unforeseen consequences, such modesty may well have been warranted.

But what about Tony Blair? Surely as prime minister of a medium-sized country with an economic and military capacity a fraction of that of the USA, his belief in his ability to control events would have been even more realistically modest than Bill Clinton's?

Hmm. Political analyst Stephen Dyson of Wabash College analysed Blair's responses at Prime Minister's Questions – the weekly grilling by parliament that all British prime ministers have to undergo.[14] He used Hermann's methods to measure Blair's belief that he could control events, again comparing it with the average for other world leaders, as well as with other British prime ministers.

So, what did Dyson find? Blair, unlike his much more powerful friend and colleague Clinton, had a hugely inflated belief that he could control world events: in statistical terms, he was more than two standard deviations higher than other world leaders in the strength with which he held this belief. And this was not some throwback to Britain's imperial pretensions. Tony Blair's belief that he could control world events was also much higher than that of his British prime-ministerial predecessors.

Blair, in other words, suffered badly from the illusion of control that power inflates, and this was possibly a factor in the breakdown in his friendship with Clinton. But why should power have so derailed the judgement of one clever man, but not the other? To answer that question, we need to take a trip forward in time to a meeting with Tony Blair's next best American president friend – George W. Bush.

The 'cojones *summit*'

Camp David nestles among the mountains of Maryland outside Washington DC and since the Second World War has witnessed a series of casually dressed US presidents and their less comfortably attired foreign leader guests making decisions and wielding a power that shapes the lives of billions of people.

In early September 2002, Prime Minister Tony Blair and his press secretary Alastair Campbell arrived to meet George W. Bush and Vice President Dick Cheney among the enchanting yellows and russets of Maryland's early fall. Blair came nursing the fond illusion that 'my job is to steer them (the Americans) in a sensible path', as Alastair Campbell reported in his diary.[15] But Bush and Cheney had already decided to invade Iraq – all they needed from Blair was his public support and his earnest eloquence on the world stage.

Campbell and Blair had a close, macho relationship, with Campbell seeming to see himself as a straight-talking equal rather than a subservient lackey. Another of Blair's senior aides, Jonathan Powell, describes how, while they were all closeted together for long periods during the crucial negotiations that brought peace to Northern Ireland, Blair and Campbell joined forces to repeatedly taunt Powell about his weight like a pair of fraternity jocks.[16]

US journalist Bob Woodward writes that, at the Camp David meeting, Bush came out of a meeting with Blair, solemnly took Campbell aside, and said, 'Your guy's got *cojones*' ('balls' in Spanish) and from then this crucial meeting was known to Bush's team as the '*cojones* summit'.[17]

Listening to Campbell read his own diaries in the audiobook version of his book, the *cojones* anecdote, which he also recounts, comes across with an irony-free solemnity that makes it clear that it is not only his boss's balls that are being praised – but, by frat-boy association – his too. It is equally clear to the casual listener – particularly in the light of subsequent revelations – that Bush and Cheney sensed that they could readily snare Blair and Campbell by pressing this very big macho button that wires straight into the pleasure centres of the brain.

After all, in Blair–Campbell frat-speak, their highest praise was to describe someone as 'ballsy'. In his autobiography *A Journey*, Blair bestows his equivalent of a hormonal knight-hood on Campbell by describing an admiration for his own press secretary's 'clanking great balls'. In that same work, Blair even manages to express admiration for the *cojones* of right-wing media mogul Rupert Murdoch. Blair was clearly proud of his own virility and flaunted it, to the extent that his book was nominated for an award for bad sex writing for its description of an amorous night with his wife Cherie.

Sex and power are linked as they both cause a surge in the hormone testosterone, as we saw in the previous chapter. High testosterone levels further increase the appetite for power and sex, in a politico-erotic vicious circle. But these appetites don't just stimulate a hunger for more power and more sex – they also have profound effects on the way the brain functions more generally.

Testosterone changes the brain because it alters its chemistry. In particular it boosts levels of the neurotransmitter dopamine. Dopamine is a key element in motivation – in getting clear in our minds what we want, and setting out to get it. Winning changes how we feel and think by racking up testosterone and the dopamine-sensitive brain systems responsible for an action-oriented approach.

And we need leaders who are motivated and goal-focused in this way – these are the essential qualities of leadership in politics, business and war. A political leader like Winston Churchill, a business magnate like Rupert Murdoch and a military general like Dwight Eisenhower would not have achieved their respective victories without this action-oriented approach to imposing their will on world events. And as we saw in the previous chapter, such successes mean that leaders constantly experience further boosts in testosterone, giving rise to the powerful success spiral of the winner effect.

One consequence of such power is that it makes us, in a certain sense, smarter. The prefrontal cortex of the brain is the seat of the brain's 'executive' – the general manager responsible for planning, forethought, setting goals, and then seeing them through. This CEO–prefrontal cortex analogy is a reasonably apt one: neither the CEO nor the prefrontal cortex are inclined to get their metaphorical hands dirty with the everyday operations which they delegate to people/brain areas lower down the hierarchy.

Both operate at a strategic level, setting rules and goals as much as following them. And both have to sort things out when events don't go to plan or when the normal routines get fouled up. It is no coincidence, then, that we describe what the prefrontal cortex does as 'executive function'.

Pamela Smith and her colleagues at Radboud University in Nijmegen in the Netherlands wanted to see what happened to these high-level thinking skills when people were made powerful or powerless in an experiment.[18] The participants were randomly assigned to be a 'superior' or a 'subordinate' in a computer-based task. The superior would not only direct the subordinate, but would also evaluate them, and this evaluation formed the basis for how much subordinates would be paid for taking part in the study, the superiors being paid a fixed amount. Even though this was an experiment, the subordinates really did experience some powerlessness, and the superiors power.

Intriguingly, the superiors made significantly fewer errors on several different tests of executive function – power and the lack of it had, in other words, crucially altered certain key cognitive functions.

You might be able to think of a time in your own life – say, the first day in a new job, or during an interview – when it seemed to you that your brain had seized up and you made mistakes and seemed unable to take in what was being said to you. Part of the reason for this are the effects of anxiety, but you were probably made temporarily less smart by the powerlessness of being assessed by people you did not know.

Power, then, primes the brain into an action mode which helps us to focus on setting goals for ourselves and achieving them – it puts us into a positive mode of thinking where we are oriented towards solving problems rather than worrying about what might go wrong.

And power shapes the brain in another, crucially important way that helps explain Tony Blair's gung-ho 'ballsy' perform-ance at the '*cojones* summit'. Ana Guinote of University College London[19] showed that power focuses attention so that people with even a little bit of power are less likely to be put off by distractors in their peripheral vision – power, in other words, puts blinkers on us – or at least, attentional blinkers.

This is part of the testosterone-triggered, dopamine-mediated can-do orientation that we admire so much in successful lead-ers. Their 'ballsiness' is partly caused by a literal 'screening out' of distractors that would otherwise sidetrack them from the big picture. While this might help in driving forward an agenda, it can also blind the leader to apparently peripheral signals and events which would otherwise be important warning signs.

Tony Blair's falling-out with Bill Clinton may have happened partly because the US president was too ready to detect these peripheral warning signs that signalled the complexities and possible downsides of military action in the Balkans. George W. Bush, on the other hand, had little problem ignoring the complexities of potentially distracting peripheral signals. As soon as Blair had dispensed with the no-longer powerful Clinton after he had left office, Blair and Bush together forged an action-oriented, testosterone-fuelled interventionist world view, undis-tracted by warning signs at the periphery of political and mili-tary vision.

The cautious accountant

Leaders who are all action, relentlessly pursuing their goals without noticing peripheral warning signals, and accruing more and more power that stokes up illusions of control and an appetite for ever more control, eventually come to grief, Napoleon and Hitler being among the most extreme examples of such hubris.

We would never have survived as a species, however, if we had evolved only to be testosterone- and dopamine-fuelled, action-oriented go-getters. Most stable, functioning governments and successful businesses that have such an action-man CEO in charge make sure that there also is a quietly spoken caution-monger counterpart – often an accountant or lawyer – somewhere in the hierarchy to impose a degree of restraint.

The similarities between the executive part of the brain and the executive running a large organisation don't stop at their roles in planning and setting goals. A further parallel is that the brain does indeed have the equivalent of a cautious accountant, working in the background, scanning the horizon for potential threats and monitoring closely what's going on.

This anxiety-prone official is located on the right half of the prefrontal cortex. This person may not wield the sort of active power in the organisation that the CEO does – and that is no bad thing: low power broadens the focus of attention to take in signals – and warnings. The cautious accountant, unlike his gung-ho, power-wielding boss, does not have the attentional blinkers that render the CEO partially blind. The cautious accountant won't be good at setting the corporate goals and setting out single-mindedly to achieve them – he'll be distracted, among other things by the peripheral signals that his boss doesn't see – and will be less motivated because he has not deluded himself into believing he has control over events that neither he nor his boss has.

The right prefrontal cortex has a predilection for a quite different chemical messenger than the dopamine of its gung-ho partner – its favoured neurochemical cocktail is *noradrenaline*, a close cousin of adrenaline but playing a bigger role in the brain. While dopamine is linked to action towards a goal and *reward* for achieving it, noradrenaline is a chemical linked to vigilance, monitoring and response to *threat*. In my own laboratory, my colleagues and I have shown how a variant of the gene that controls noradrenaline levels in the brain is linked to vigilant, watchful behaviour in real life, and that this in turn is linked to activity in the right half of the prefrontal cortex.[20]

When the right prefrontal cortex is alerted to potential threat, it widens the focus of attention – like a broad radar-sweep of the skyline to check for danger. Powerlessness is a sort of threat, so it makes sense that people without power should be more inclined to scan the horizon for the threat of unforeseen events that they cannot control. The left prefrontal cortex does the opposite when geared up for action – it focuses attention on the goal, in a similar way to that in which power puts on the attentional blinkers. Power, then, may unbalance our very ability to recognise risk, as well as our inclination to take heed of it.

Had the action-oriented dopamine and cautious-accountant noradrenaline systems of Tony Blair's brain become somewhat out of kilter – and further disrupted by the power he apparently sought by associating himself so closely with the new president of the United States when they first met in February 2001? Was the delicate counter-weighting of approach and caution disrupted by the surges of dopamine that the power-generated testosterone triggered in a prime minister so obviously preoccupied with 'ballsiness'.

Blair's early military successes and his political success in achieving near-total dominance over his cabinet would likely have increased the dopamine levels in his brain, which would in turn have narrowed his attention to the goals he saw as important. Bill Clinton, on the other hand, would have undergone less of a chemical transformation of his brain. And while Blair's chemically induced narrowing of attention would have diminished his recognition of the risks in Kosovo, Clinton's less power-altered brain would have been all too aware of the Vietnam-type possibilities that lay in a ground invasion of the brutal mountains of Kosovo. Blair's cowed ministerial colleagues, because of their relative powerlessness in the cabinet, would have had their appetite for opposing Blair's power dulled – something that was much less of an issue among Clinton's fractious advisers.

In the last years of Tony Blair's prime ministership, I spoke with one of his top advisers. The man was very defensive of his boss during our conversation, but his guard went down once. 'It's his constant *certainty* that worries me,' he frowned and muttered. Such a sense of unwavering certainty is a symptom of a brain fired up with dopamine, focused on action, and with a reduced capacity for self-scrutiny or caution. The world is too complex for certainty – and a political leader who feels such certainty should make us a little anxious. Certainty in the face of the unpredictable complexity of the world can run the risk of being delusional. Power causes illusions of control and puts blinkers on a person. Tony Blair was likely more afflicted than Bill Clinton, and that played a part in the breach in their friendship. But why was Tony Blair's mind so much more changed by power than was his ex-friend's? To really get to the bottom of the enigma, this is the final puzzle we have to solve.

*   *   *

I'd like you to write a short story, a paragraph of around fifty words maximum. It won't take long, just a few minutes, and you should write it without planning or thinking too much. Base it on one of two imagined images – either a bearded ship's captain gazing out to sea from the deck of a passenger liner, or a small group of women standing around wearing white coats in a laboratory. Now write a short story based on one of these imagined pictures.

Afterwards, take a look at your story and have a stab at analysing it. Make a mark on the paper or in the onscreen document to indicate where your imagined characters do or show any of the following:

• Carry out strong, psychologically or physically forceful, actions.
• Provide help or advice without being asked for it.
• Try to regulate or control what others are doing.
• Try to influence, bribe or argue with another person.
• Seek to impress.
• Arouse strong reactions or emotions in others in a one-sided way.
• Are concerned with prestige and/or reputation.

Professor D.G. Winter of the University of Michigan devised this method for assessing people's motives through analysing the images contained in their stories.[21] When different raters used his manual to count the number of instances of the types of themes that you assessed in your stories, they had a high degree of agreement: in other words, it is possible scientifically and reliably to measure an individual's underlying motives by analysing the content of what they say and write.

We can't get under the skin of people's motives by asking them: our motives are largely unconscious and what we say about what drives us is often shaped by our notions about what is acceptable, and by our general conscious image of ourselves. But when we actually do things in the world – or indeed when our proxy imaginary characters act in our stories, then it is possible to get a glimpse into the murky world of our largely unconscious motives.

Winter's system, then, can assess reliably different types of motive – and the one which you have just measured in your own story is the power motive – *the need for power*.

Take a moment to think about some of your friends, family and colleagues. Which among them would you consider are motivated by power? By this I mean they seem to be motivated to have an *impact* on other people. For instance, they might like to give orders, make the decisions, take control and so on – they are *action*-oriented. Equally, their actions can be in the form of giving – advice, gifts and directions, for instance. 'Impact' also refers to having an effect on people – persuading them, or changing their emotions by, for instance, surprising or shocking them. Finally, having an impact involves having a particularly strong concern with your own reputation.

Let's take a look at one of Tony Blair's early speeches on foreign policy, which he gave on 15 December 1998, during his second year in power: 'I have said before that though Britain will never be the mightiest nation on earth, we can be pivotal. It means building on the strengths of our history; it means building new alliances; developing new influence; charting a new course for British foreign policy. It means realising once and for all that Britain does not have to choose between being strong with the US, or strong with Europe; it means having the confidence to see that Britain can be both.'

Blair's focus on having impact, influence and strength – of having a pivotal role in shaping history – could not be clearer. It is hard to imagine the leaders of many medium-sized countries assuming that their role, or the role of any single country, could be 'pivotal' in the context of world events. His text is replete with action verbs, of shaping and influencing, not just events in Britain, but the future of humanity. And this is not selective reporting. His autobiography *A Journey* consistently focuses on this very strong desire he demonstrates for changing and controlling processes and events. At one point he complains about the 'rubber levers' of government, which bent when he pulled them but had, to his eyes at least, little impact. Throughout his time as prime minister, he strove to create systems and inner circles which could stiffen up the rubber levers and give him personal control over political and social events and policy.

Without this in many ways admirable focus on action, impact and results, it is unlikely that peace in Northern Ireland would have been achieved, to give one example. Positive action is preferable to passive inaction in a leader. But the issue here is the psychology of the man and the degree to which he was driven by this need, this hunger for power.

We saw earlier how political analyst Stephen Dyson of Wabash College analysed Blair's responses during Prime Minister's Questions, when the leader of the government must respond without prior notice of the topic to questions on any subject that Members of Parliament can throw at him. Using Margaret Hermann's methods to measure Blair's belief that he could control events and again comparing it with the average for other world leaders, as well as with other British prime ministers, Dyson carried out the same analysis on Blair's need for power.

What emerged was that Blair, unlike his in reality much more powerful friend and colleague Bill Clinton, had a higher need for power: he was an outlier among world leaders, with a need for power higher than *98 per cent* of these already highly power-motivated politicians. And what about Bill Clinton? He was, according to another analysis by Margaret Hermann, at an average level in terms of this motivation, hungering for power to a degree comparable to the average for other world leaders, in spite of the objectively greater economic, military and political power at his disposal.[22]

Is this, then, the crux of the solution to the enigma of Bill Clinton's friend: was it that their motivations were fundamentally different? Tony Blair had a deep-seated hunger for power that Bill Clinton did not share to nearly the same extent. Did this lead to fundamentally different political judgements and policies? Possibly. We saw earlier how power changes brain function by narrowing attention, increasing an illusory sense of control and boosting motivation to achieve goals. But Bill Clinton had much more power than Tony Blair did, so why shouldn't his brain have been just as, if not more, altered by power?

The killer instinct

I somehow doubt that Tony Blair and Bill Clinton ever played computer games against each other. Let's imagine, however, that we have got them together to do so – a simple game where they have to press a button as soon as a target appears on the screen, and try to be faster than the other person. They play for around ten minutes, and we take a saliva swab from each of them before and after the game.

The saliva swab lets us measure the levels of the stress hormone cortisol, which, as we saw earlier, the body releases into the blood during stressful situations like interviews, exams, arguments or fights. And why are we interested in Blair and Clinton's stress levels? We are interested because their differing needs for power suggest that their bodies and brains will respond differently to winning and losing.

So what precisely is being predicted? That, because of his very high need for power, Tony Blair's cortisol level will shoot up if he loses, but fall if he wins. Bill Clinton, because of his less power-hungry psychological make-up, will find losing less stressful, his blood will be less infused with cortisol if he loses, and his cortisol level will fall less than Blair's if he wins.

I make this prediction on the basis of research by Michelle Wirt and her colleagues at the University of Michigan.[23] They used the reaction time competition game with a group of male and female volunteers, but they rigged the results so that individuals were – via false feedback – allocated to a winner or a loser group.

Wirt measured need for power using the sort of methods that revealed Tony Blair's high power needs and then looked at how those with low power need and those with high power need compared in their reaction to winning and losing. Individuals whose power needs were, like Blair's, high, responded to the rigged win by big falls in their stress hormone levels. And boy, they did not like to lose – their cortisol level shot up if they were told they had lost.

Losing was much less stressful for those with lower power needs. I won't say 'like Bill Clinton' here, because while his power need was a lot lower than Blair's and only average for a world leader, world leaders are still a pretty power-needy bunch, so Clinton was only relatively lower than Blair in this motivation.

What is particularly intriguing about Wirt's results, however, is what happened to the stress hormone levels of low power need individuals when they won. Winning made their cortisol level rise – for them, victory was stressful.

You may already noticed something like this phenomenon if you play sport. Some people have the 'killer instinct' – that motivation to drive home an advantage and win the game. Others inexplicably find themselves wilting on the cusp of victory and letting their opponent defeat them. The sporting killer instinct may reflect the need for power, and the prospect of dominating another may trigger in someone with low power needs an unconscious aversion to finishing off their opponent and winning the match.

Threat and appeasement in the human jungle

Modern brain-imaging methods confirm that the unconscious need for power is a real feature of how our brains work. Let's take day-to-day interchanges between people in politics or business. Consciously or not, we are involved in a constant monitoring of our place in the pecking order as we meet different people of varying social or business ranks. And the expressions on our faces are one of the most important signals as to what our current position is: if the big boss walks in, for instance, witness the deferential smiles and modestly averted gaze of his/her underlings.

In the day-to-day threat and appeasement displays of the social and business jungle, facial expression is one of the most important signals of where we stand in the pecking order. A colleague's angry face, for instance, might give us pause as it could signal that we are being challenged for having overstepped our position. A surprised face, on the other hand, signals to us that we have had an impact on that person.

Power-needy people are particularly attuned to facial signals of the impact they are having, and Oliver Schultheiss and his colleagues at the University of Michigan have unveiled the different brain processes that underpin these different levels of power motivation.[24]

Schultheiss used brain imaging – fMRI – to study the reaction of men and women with different levels of power need to pictures of angry, surprised and neutral faces. True to the prediction, the people with a high need for power showed a much stronger activation of brain areas responsible for emotion, bodily sensations and reward. The angry faces seemed to cause a much stronger 'gut reaction' in the high-power-need individuals, and kicked into gear the brain regions in the striatum and lower surface of the frontal lobes that are constantly working out the reward value of things and situations.

A person's need for power is a pretty important factor in shaping how they conduct themselves, yet it is not something that is uppermost in our minds as we think about others. We are more likely to consider classic personality features such as whether someone is introverted or extraverted, anxious or emotionally stable, but we don't think about a factor which can have a much bigger effect on our lives – a person's need for power.

This applies to marriage and relationships as much as it does to politics and government; it is as crucial a feature in the workplace as it is in the school or club. It even applies to sex: people with a high need for power – both men and women – on average have sexual intercourse more often than their low-power-need friends,[25] and climb up the career ladder more quickly than less power-hungry colleagues.

On the downside, men with high power needs are more likely to abuse their female partners – particularly if the woman has more financial or status power in the relationship. If you look around at the people you spend time with – neighbours, workmates, friends or family – the small-p politics of these groups will be hugely determined by the various levels of need for power in the individuals concerned. Some individuals will strive to dominate – there is a good chance they may not even be aware of this – and they may do so for the best of reasons. But be sure of this: your peace of mind and well-being depend largely on your relationships with other people, and in turn these relationships are shaped by the various individual power needs more strongly than by any other factor.

And when it comes to big-P politics, the effects of the need for power on your life are multiplied extraordinarily: Would the Iraq War have taken place had Tony Blair's unusually high need for power not driven him to support George W. Bush's plans? Bush did not need Britain militarily, but he *did* need Blair's political support both internally and externally. Had Blair opposed the war, perhaps the US Congress would have been emboldened to ask hard questions of their president rather than give him the military free pass which many Congressmen and Congresswomen later regretted?

One of the biggest dangers for the world comes from that surge of testosterone coursing into the blood of the high-power-need leader after he *wins*. That hormonal surge is intoxicating. Like the mountaineer seeking the fix of the next and more dangerous peak, the power-primed politician finds it hard to cope with the mundanity of day-to-day politics – he yearns for that chemical high that winning triggers in him. Unfortunately, like all such highs, the next stimulus has to be stronger to get the same effect.

Political leaders who have a high psychological need for power tend to run their governments through small inner circles, bypassing established cabinet and committee systems. In this way, they feel they can exert the power they dearly want to deploy. Leaders with low or average levels of power need, on the other hand, are more inclined to delegate, consult and seek consensus from their cabinets and officials. Decision making can be slow under such leaders, but the diversity of views so abhorred by the power-hungry leader can prevent decisions being made which are later regretted.

Tony Blair was famous for his extremely short cabinet meetings, where ministers were essentially informed about decisions made elsewhere and yet, as I mentioned earlier, he still complained about the 'rubber levers' of government which bent when he pulled them, sabotaging his great need for impact.

Blair's high need for power had both good and bad effects. His close involvement in, and control over, Northern Ireland policy was a key factor leading to the peace process there. He also had some noble victories as a frequently interventionist world leader hungry for impact. With drug-crazed rebels lopping off the limbs of babies and children in Sierra Leone, Blair sent a military task force which stabilised the country, saving thousands of lives and leading to the trial of the rebel leader Charles Taylor before the International War Crimes Tribunal. And against the opposition of sluggish European politicians whose self-interest and indolence had allowed tens of thousands to die brutal deaths in Bosnia, he intervened militarily with the USA in Kosovo and forestalled another bout of Balkan genocide.

Blair's insistence, however, on advancing a minority position and sending British troops to invade Iraq is thought by many to have been a mistake and a major failure of democratic control over prime-ministerial action. Whether Blair would have engaged in the Iraq adventure had his brain not been changed by the chemistry of power and the testosterone surges of successive victories is a question of counter-factual speculation that no one can answer with confidence. What is clear, however, is that neither the huge political talent of Tony Blair, nor his considerable moral courage, nor membership of a liberal social-democratic political party could protect him from the effects that power had on his brain. And nor could a deep friendship with his less power-affected friend Bill Clinton survive that chemistry.

Democracy, one of civilisation's inspired inventions, evolved to serve one major purpose – to protect us and our children from the brain-altering chemistry of power and its consequences. Tony Blair lasted ten years as prime minister. With no maximum term defined, Blair could have continued for longer were it not for the democratic pressures of a political-party system in which pressure can be exerted even on the head man or woman in the country. It was these pressures that eased a reluctant Blair from high office.

Such pressures are considerably diluted in the case of another prime minister – Silvio Berlusconi of Italy – who survived long in office by virtue of controlling a vast media and television empire that helped to deliver him the necessary votes. Democracy only extends to a minority of the globe, but even where it does have a hold, its proper operation is often distorted by the manipulation of public opinion by the mass media. In the case of Berlusconi, his parliament passed a new law which decriminalised a crime with which he had been charged – false accounting – leading to accusations that it was passed just to acquit him. His Bacchanalian parties with young, scantily clad women, widely reported during 2009, also show that the power–sex link endures well into the sunset years.

Dominique Strauss-Kahn is another powerful man, rated by *Forbes* magazine the thirty-seventh most powerful person in the world[26] before that fateful day of 14 May 2011, when he was taken off an Air France jet at JFK Airport, New York, to be charged with sexual assault, a charge which was subsequently dropped. On 31 October 2010, *Newsweek* ran a feature on him:

'Dominique Strauss-Kahn is on top of the world just now . . . Almost by default the managing director of the International Monetary Fund keeps accruing power in the midst of crisis,' the magazine wrote about the then hot favourite to win the 2012 French presidential election.

There was one other and rather prescient paragraph in *Newsweek*'s piece: 'Before DSK [Dominique Strauss-Kahn] went to Washington, a columnist for the Paris daily *Libération* cautioned that his "only real problem" there could be was "the way he relates to women".' Known in his homeland France as the 'Great Seducer', Strauss-Kahn had lived up to his nickname after only a few months in this powerful job which he took up in 2007. In January 2008 he admitted an affair with a young woman subordinate in the IMF. Subsequently, it was reported by a friend of the woman, IMF economist Piroska Nagy, with whom he had the affair, that while it was consensual, '. . .she [Nagy] had felt coerced because Mr Strauss-Kahn was so forceful and so senior to her, making it hard for her to, in effect, say no'.[27]

Had DSK not had a sexual liaison with his hotel chambermaid in 2011, he had a very strong chance of becoming president of France. Under the French constitution, the French president has immunity from legal action in French courts while in office. Given what we know about the relationship between power and sex, we can only wonder how 'the way he relates to women' would have developed in the absence of the threat of any legal sanction on his behaviour if he had become president.

Vladimir Putin is another world leader whose need for power is clear, and who has presided over a government which has considerably weakened the mechanisms of democratic society – independent media and judicial process among them. If, as expected, Putin becomes president again in 2012 and, as is also likely, serves two terms in office, he will have held power in Russia for almost a quarter of a century as either president or prime minister. This former head of the KGB's taste for photographs of himself, often bare-chested, with tigers and bears,[28] may have political and electoral significance, but it is hard to avoid the conclusion that they are also signs that long-term power has had significant effects on President Putin's brain.

Yet Angela Merkel, Chancellor of Germany, in 2011 ranked by *Forbes* as the sixth most powerful person in the world and the world's most powerful woman,[29] appears, superficially at least, to be relatively free of the symptoms of power's effects on the brain in her demeanour and actions, unlike some of her male peers in Italy, Russia, the UK and France mentioned above. During the Eurozone crisis of 2011, in fact, a common criticism was that she failed to offer the sort of strong leadership needed to provide a united response to the crisis, and seemed excessively tied by the constitutional and parliamentary constraints of the German political system in her decision making. Whether this is a coincidence, or whether gender plays a part in power's effects on the brain, is something I will come back to in Chapter 5.

Most people who drink alcohol do not become addicted to it. Their consumption is regulated by ritual, by a focus on taste over intoxication, by combining it with food and so on. It is when these constraints are stripped away and large quantities are consumed in order to get drunk that addiction sets in. This is also true for political power. When exercised against the constraints and rituals of democratic institutions, its infusion into the blood of leaders is regulated and addiction can be avoided. It is only when the raw liquor of power hits the blood of someone with a high need for it, that the really big problems arise.

We are all different – some of us have a need for power, others less so. The world needs leaders who have a desire to change things, to have an impact. A need for power is not in itself a bad thing – teachers, psychologists, physicians, managers, campaigners are all driven by a wish to have an impact. But problems arise when a brain primed with a high need for power is over-exposed to actual power in the real world.

Power in the hands of a high-power-need person like Tony Blair is a heady cocktail which can exaggerate the egocentric certainties of the power-affected brain. But when a low-power-need person is in senior political or business roles, they can often make excellent deputies because their conciliatory, consensus-building skills help them mediate between the power-induced insensitivities of the boss and the bruised feelings of underlings suffering under the goal-focused insensitivity of a dominant boss.

This is not to say that good leaders should not be consensus builders – quite the reverse – and in fact an ideal is to have a leader who builds consensus among his team. But an effective leader also needs a minimum level of need for power, otherwise the responsibilities of power will be too stressful. Hence, if low-power-need managers are promoted to boss, the stress they feel may flood their brains with cortisol, which can, as we will see in the next chapter, hinder good judgement.

The testosterone and other chemicals that power generates in the brain not only change thought and emotion, but are also literally addictive, particularly in people with a high need for power. Tony Blair was probably more hooked on power than Bill Clinton was, and it showed in his judgement over the Iraq War. This was likely a key factor in the breach in Blair and Clinton's friendship.

In the previous chapter we saw how we can become winners by happening to be in the right place at the right time – like the NT cichlid fish who happens to be nearby when a gull plucks an unfortunate T fish from Lake Tanganyika. In this chapter, I have shown that being given power really produces T-cichlid-fish-like changes in human beings as well, but that these changes are much more variable from person to person.

Power makes us smarter, more ambitious, more aggressive and more focused. These qualities are sharpened when we win, and they boost our chances of winning in the future. Power changes us in such a way that it opens doors in our brain that help us gain more power. Power, in other words, empowers us to be winners through a positive feedback loop, a virtuous cycle of power-induced brain changes that make us even more of a winner in the future.

This is a vivid example of the 'Matthew effect', a term inspired by the New Testament text 'to them that hath shall be given . . .'. In the previous chapter we saw how the winner effect worked – the mere fact of winning primes us to be winners in the future. In the current chapter I have shown that for human beings it is not just the fact of winning that makes us winners. More than that, it is the fact that power reshapes our brains to make us smarter and more focused, thus boosting our power and opening up for us opportunities for even more success.

But some of us have a greater sensitivity to power and are physically and psychologically changed more by it. Blair had this driving need for power which helped generate his notable early wins in Northern Ireland, Sierra Leone and Kosovo. As the world's most powerful man, Clinton was clearly no slouch in the power-need stakes, but when compared with other world leaders, his need for power was average for the breed, and much lower than Blair's.

On top of that, Clinton's early experiences in international power politics led to humiliating reverses in Somalia and Haiti, thus tempering his taste for deploying US military muscle and leaving him starved of the benefits of any winner effect in this domain. These differences in experience of success between the two leaders, combined with their profound differences in deep-seated motivation for power, almost inevitably led to the rift that Blair's Chicago speech caused.

But solving that puzzle immediately throws up another one – why do people like Tony Blair want to win so badly? What is behind this need for power? The answer to this question is far from trivial because the costs of holding power for leaders are so great. To be convinced of this, take a look at photographs of young-looking, physically fit leaders like Tony Blair, Bill Clinton, George W. Bush and Barack Obama at the start of office, and compare them with their photographs each subsequent year in leadership: in just a few short years their faces age, hair greys and foreheads become etched with the lines that are the indelible price of power.

The rapidity of the power-induced ageing process surely testifies to a set of stresses that should put us off seeking power, rather than striving for it. So what *is* it that drives some of us to sacrifice our youth to gain it? What impels people to strive for power?

That question brings us to the fourth of our mysteries – why do we want to win so badly?

4

The Mystery of the Oscars

Why do we want to win?

In 1956, MGM Studios offered the actor Charlton Heston the lead role in *Alexander the Great*, the blockbuster movie of that year. Heston was tempted but, after some agonising, turned it down for the lead in another epic, *The Ten Commandments*. His chiselled features, six-foot-four-inch frame, booming baritone voice – and of course his uncanny resemblance to Michelangelo's Moses – made him a shoo-in for the role.

But the MGM executives planning *Alexander the Great* were not too bothered by Heston's jumping ship. Why? Because they had an even bigger star in the sidelines – reputedly Hollywood's highest paid – to take the role. If anything, the replacement Richard Burton's blue-eyed good looks and honeyed voice outshone those of Heston.

While these two Hollywood hot properties may have shared good looks and meteoric careers, within three years one event was to cleave a chasm between them.

Move forward to 1959. The big movie of that year was to be *Ben-Hur,* but the MGM moguls had a problem – three of them, in fact. First they wanted Marlon Brando to play the lead, but he turned them down. Their second choice was Burt Lancaster, but he too said no. The last of the three to show them the door was Rock Hudson.[1]

In desperation the team rooted around for a suitable leading man, eventually coming up with – not a second best – but a fourth best choice. Quickly taking a decision that would change his life for ever, Charlton Heston said yes.

That yes changed his life for one crucial reason – the 1960 Academy Award he won for his lead role in *Ben-Hur*. This fourth-best choice donned his black tie and collected an Oscar.

This was the one and only time that anyone ever nominated Heston for an Oscar. Whereas, in spite of his name being put forward no fewer than seven times, Richard Burton never collected one. The spread of his nomination years – 1952, 1953, 1964, 1965, 1966, 1969 and 1977 – confirms that Burton was no flash-in-the-pan phenomenon, but rather a highly success-ful and talented performer. He is most remembered now for being twice married to Elizabeth Taylor. But this internationally acclaimed actor never got his Academy Award.

On 5 August 1984, Richard Burton died of a brain haemor-rhage. He was fifty-eight. Twenty-four years later, on 5 April 2008, Charlton Heston died. He was eighty-four. It would be tendentious to interweave these two facts – Burton's early death and Heston's Academy Award – as illustrating anything other than the particular medical status of two actors, were it not for one startling research finding: Oscar winners live on average four years longer than, by all other measures, equally successful Oscar nominees.[2]

Burton's death may have had nothing to do with his lack of Academy Award success – it is impossible to draw such conclu-sions from a single example. But the point of contrasting Burton's and Heston's fates is to illustrate a fact that *is* secure – that winning Oscars is linked to a substantial boost to one's life expectancy. In fact if such a four-year improvement in life expectancy were extrapolated to the whole population it would be equivalent to the result of curing all cancers. What's more, movie stars who win more than one Oscar live on average *six* years longer than mere nominees. What is going on here?

Before trying to answer that question, it is worth noting that this miraculous elixir is not just apparent in the glitzy world of Hollywood; it also applies to the less glamorous realm of science. Nobel Prize winners live on average one to two years longer than their colleagues who were nominated for, but not given, the coveted award.[3] As in the movie industry, the final selection among a group of more or less equally talented nominees has a fair degree of chance and politics about it, but that spotlight of fame and recognition seems to affect the bodies and brains of the winners in a truly remarkable way. Why?

It is this mystery of how a symbolic award like an Oscar or a Nobel Prize can lengthen someone's life which I set out to solve here. The answer is important because an understanding of this life-extending benefit of winning can lead us to an answer to another question – *why* do people want to win so badly?

The dead towers of Glasgow

When the American novelist Nathaniel Hawthorne visited the Scottish city of Glasgow in 1857, he wrote, 'I am inclined to think that Glasgow is the stateliest city I have ever beheld.' His visit coincided with Glasgow's status as one of the most significant cities of the British Empire – perhaps a little like Shanghai is to China today – and one of the wealthiest cities in Europe owing to its thriving industry and feverish trade with the rest of the world.

You can catch a glimpse of that past wealth if you glance up the hill above the Cathedral to one of Glasgow's more peaceful quarters, the Necropolis – a sprawling graveyard that dominates the city's skyline. This strange and silent suburb of the dead is a cityscape of soot-blackened mansions for the corpses who once drove central Scotland's white-hot economy.

The mausoleums – some two storeys high – are surrounded by graves, and marking a large number of these are stone obelisks. In the Necropolis, as well as across the graveyards of nineteenth-century Glasgow, these obelisks present a series of vistas scarcely less strange than the stone statues of Easter Island in the Pacific, or the medieval towers of the Tuscan town of San Gimignano.

And just as the Easter Island statues and San Gimignano's towers vary in height, so do the obelisks. But their standard shape means that you can, simply by measuring their height, tell something very important about the people buried below them. One assumption that can be made is that the size of the monument reflected the wealth and social status of the deceased and their families. Using the height of these obelisks as a proxy for wealth and social status, epidemiologist George Davey Smith and his colleagues at the University of Glasgow discovered that it is a predictable indicator of the age at which the poor souls buried below them died – the higher the obelisk, the longer the life.[4] That the rich live longer than the poor is not perhaps surprising, but the very poor could not have afforded even a tiny obelisk, and so the linkage between tombstone height and lifespan had emerged out of the gradation in wealth even among the comparatively well-off citizens of this once thriving city.

Is this, then, an answer to the puzzle of the long-living Oscar winners? Is it just a question of wealth? Did Charlton Heston survive to eighty-four because he could pamper himself with the luxuries and fine living that the Oscar triggered? This does not seem particularly likely. After all, many box-office-bursting movies do not generate Oscars: earnings and awards do not necessarily go hand in hand. Remember also that, as well as having seven Best Actor nominations, Richard Burton was reputedly the highest-paid Hollywood actor in the 1950s. But we need harder data than that to make sure the mystery of the Oscars is not simply solved by money. To find such evidence, we have to travel to the home of the Nobel Prize, to Stockholm.

Winning the Nobel Prize is not only a great honour, it is also lucrative – in 2008 the value of the prize was just under US$1.5 million. This is only a little higher than its equivalent in 1901, at just under $1.2 million. But for much of the twentieth century, between about 1920 and the late 1980s, the prize languished at approximately a quarter of its 2008 value, at less than the equivalent of $400,000. So Nobel Prize winners at the beginning and end of the twentieth century stood to become much richer than their equally esteemed colleagues in the middle of the century.

Unlike Hollywood stars, however, Nobel-level scientists are not rich and most live quiet lives sustained by modest university salaries – so the impact of a Nobel Prize on their personal finances is massive. If the answer to the mystery of the Oscars is money, then for the equivalent Nobel effect – winners living one to two years longer on average than nominees – we should see the millionaire prize winners living substantially longer than those who won less than $400,000.

Matthew Rablen and Andrew Oswald of the University of Warwick in England were able to put this hypothesis to the test by retrieving the birth and death dates of 532 Nobel Prize nominees in Chemistry and Physics between 1901 and 1950.[5] (This is the best they could do, as the Nobel Foundation keeps the names of both nominators and nominees secret for fifty years.) So what was the outcome? Did sudden millionairedom give a boost to the lifespan of these dedicated, hard-working scientists? No, it did not. Wealth, as measured by the value of the prize, did not matter; it was the bald fact of winning that prolonged their lives.

Business life may seem a long way from the academic halls of Stockholm and the Nobel Prize, but there may be lessons for business. Given the dramatic effects of such accolades, is it possible that an excessively bonus-oriented culture might dilute the motivating effect of symbolic achievements such as the Academy and Nobel awards? If I do an exceptionally good job as an executive and receive a very large financial bonus for this, there is the strong possibility that I might *attribute* my motivation to the money rather than to my own intrinsic drive. There is also *cognitive dissonance* at play, a common but largely unconscious mental glitch. I will explain this more fully in Chapter 6, but cognitive dissonance works something like this.

The human mind is motivated to reduce incompatibility between what it thinks and feels on the one hand, and how it behaves on the other. Where it detects such inconsistency, it often 'rationalises' by changing the thought and associated feeling to be consistent with the behaviour. For instance, having been induced to spend time in volunteer work, you might find yourself concluding: 'I've just spent a day working very hard for no pay to help a local charity shop, so I must really care about it.' It can also work in more fundamental aspects of our lives, such as: 'I have just married this man, so I must really love him.'

Carol Dweck's work at Yale, which I described in Chapter 1, considered the question of intrinsic versus external rewards for good behaviour in children. She found that giving material or monetary rewards to children for doing school tasks that they were already interested in actually reduced their motivation and enjoyment of the task. Cognitive dissonance was probably at work here. 'Why am I doing this? They are paying me, so it must be because I don't enjoy it.'

There are many domains of human endeavour where people get enormous satisfaction – a sense of reward which fires up their brains' dopamine systems – from doing a job well, contributing to a cause or achieving a goal. The respect and admiration of others is an even more potent source of dopamine reward in the brain. The approval of a respected boss can be more intrinsically rewarding for an employee than a financial bonus. The approval symbolised by an Oscar or a Nobel Prize will beat any sum of money.

Let's go back to the Nobel Prize winners and their extra year or two of life. This may not sound like very much but, as Rablen and Oswald point out, these 532 nominees were already of very high status. Fêted by colleagues at conferences throughout the world, respected and admired in their home towns and universities, they already had considerable social advantages over their less august colleagues. So for there to be an *average* of one to two years added to their lifespans by simply winning a prize is a huge and remarkable effect. Not quite as big as the Oscars effect – the equivalent of curing all cancers – but still very, very big.

If the enormous accolade of an Oscar or Nobel Prize can deliver such life-expanding benefits in a group of people already bathed in the approval and attention of many, it seems plausible to presume that even modest accolades could have potentially considerable effects on people who are much less socially advantaged than high-performing scientists and famous movie stars. As we scan the grey-black rows of towers in Glasgow's Necropolis, and the longer-living Nobel Prize winners, it is clear that the mystery of the Oscars cannot be put down to the benefits of wealth. Something else must be extending their lives, and that something, perhaps, also led to the Glasgow people buried below the tallest towers living longer.

So the answer to the mystery of the Oscars is not wealth; but what *is* this elixir of youth?

Politicians and baboons

It is pre-9/11 2001 in Washington DC. Sir Christopher Meyer, British Ambassador to the USA, makes his customary diary notes, recording his impressions of the day's guests passing through what he lovingly and repeatedly calls 'The Great House'.[6] This is the British Ambassador's residence next to the US Vice President's Naval Observatory residence on Embassy Row – coveted by every British diplomat.

The First Minister of Scotland, Henry McLeish, was visiting Washington and Meyer noted that McLeish was 'struck nearly dumb with shock' when, to his astonishment, he discovered he had been invited to meet President Bush at the White House. Meyer goes on: 'As poor Henry twitched and stuttered in the Oval Office, George W. Bush, accompanied by the then National Security Advisor, Condoleezza Rice, genially recounted stories of Bush's time in Scotland as a boy.'

McLeish subsequently wrote an article about his visit for the British *Parliamentary Monitor* journal, which the journalist Paul Routledge described as reading like a schoolboy's 'What I Did on My Holiday' essay. 'What did I make of the president?' McLeish wrote. 'Very personable and impressive. Is the Oval Office really oval? Yes it is.'[7]

The African baboon is a pretty tough beast whose two-inch-long canines allow it a rich and varied diet ranging from plant roots and crabs to young antelope. These evolutionary cousins of ours can put to rout whole herds of jackals – only leopards really scare them. They also have quite complex social arrangements which involve some baboons having long-term high-ranking positions in the troop and others having more humble stations.

As they travel across the savannah, the dominant males take the lead, with the females and young in the middle, and the low-ranking foot soldier baboons lurking at the rear, staying clear of the bosses up front. This avoidance is because it is pretty stressful for a low-ranking baboon to interact with a top animal – so stressful, in fact, that in some groups a male of inferior status will pick up an infant (any one will do) and proffer it as a sort of placating totem to the dominant male if he meets him. The hope is that, instead of sinking his sharp canines into the interloper, the boss will go gooey at the sight of the baby. But babies aren't always available and even with such ruses, interactions between baboons are stressful for the subordinate animal. And stress triggers the flow of a very important hormone into their blood.

As I mentioned in Chapter 2, the hormone cortisol is a sort of supercharger that baboons, humans and other animals have as part of their body's emergency response system, with the aid of adrenaline and other substances, helping get them out of trouble when threatened and hence stressed. Cortisol is the first-line stress hormone, pumping glucose into blood and brain to induce faster responses to an emergency. Adrenaline is also triggered by stress, quickening your pulse, raising your blood pressure, sucking blood from your innards out into your primed-for-action muscles and generally making you fired up and ready to jump. Cortisol also changes your immune system's operation and suppresses your digestive system.

Subordinate baboons, with some exceptions, have cortisol swirling in their bloodstreams because of their repeated stressful encounters with more dominant animals in their troop, the great US biologist Robert Sapolsky has shown.[8] Similarly, as Henry McLeish walked into the Oval Office to meet George W. Bush, his blood would have filled with cortisol, his heart pumping and his skin clammy with the activity of a ramped-up peripheral nervous system. He probably also felt like he had to go to the bathroom – unburdening your body of unnecessary weight makes it easier to escape the bite of a dominant male.

More importantly, parts of Henry's brain would have been disrupted by the cortisol, particularly the memory centres deep in the hippocampus, and also in the frontal lobes, which control self-awareness and inhibition. Henry's memory of his meeting with the President is therefore probably a bit of a blur because his moment-to-moment memory system would have been malfunctioning, as would his ability to attend to what he was doing. No wonder his memoirs of the occasion were confined to confirming the shape of the Oval Office. Henry's brain's 'brake' – the inhibition system in the right half of the outside surface of the frontal lobe, just under his sweaty right temple – would also have been running a little roughly, so he almost certainly said things that he later regretted. A reminder of what this looks like from the outside can be given by watching job candidates waiting for an interview, or the TV Apprentices sitting at a table waiting for judgement to be pronounced on them by the UK's Sir Alan Sugar or the USA's Donald Trump.

Sir Christopher gives another vivid description of a stressed, un-braked brain running free in the case of a second UK politician visiting Washington. The cortisol-intoxicated politician in this instance was John Prescott, Tony Blair's amiable, loyal but not particularly linguistically gifted Deputy Prime Minister. The Ambassador notes that Prescott took his status as Deputy Prime Minister very seriously and was adamant that he should see Vice President Cheney to discuss the full range of foreign policy challenges of the moment. The problem was that, according to Sir Christopher, 'he never appeared to be sufficiently up on the issues and he always seemed nervous'. Sir Christopher would 'will him on as he sank lower in his chair and talked faster and faster', while a US senator with long military experience was somewhat surprised to hear Mr Prescott announce that British Harrier jets were bombing from a height of fifteen feet, and that their action was crucial to the fate of 'the Balklands'.

Thanks to a study by Caroline Zink and others at the US National Institute of Health, we now have a pretty good idea about what may have been going on in Henry McLeish's and John Prescott's brains during their meetings with the US President and his Vice President.[9] Zink and her colleagues created artificial social hierarchies in which volunteers played competitive games in the presence of people who were prominently classified as three-, two- or one-star players. Even in this artificial social hierarchy, 'meeting' someone of higher status generated a lot of extra activity in precisely those parts of the brain – the areas of the dorso-lateral prefrontal cortex – which are involved in planning what you are going to say, listening to yourself as you say it, and stopping yourself from saying something inappropriate.

The jargon for this is 'self-monitoring', and the right outside front surface of the brain is central to this most essential of human abilities – self-awareness. One of the commonest ways of dulling self-awareness is to drink alcohol, and it is in part due to alcohol's dampening effects on self-awareness and self-monitoring that people write, say and do things that they may bitterly regret the next morning. 'Oh no, I didn't say that to the boss, did I?'

So, the rabbit-in-the-headlights behaviour of Henry McLeish and John Prescott may have been in part because the critical

THE MYSTERY OF THE OSCARS

part of their brain's self-awareness machinery was jammed up with the task of dealing with their high-status interlocutor. This explains why many people burble star-struck nonsense when they encounter someone famous. They are in essence rendered temporarily drunk by the brain-dulling effects of encountering someone of high status.

Henry and John's muddle and nerves were little different from how low-ranking baboons respond to meeting a high-status dominant male. Unfortunately for McLeish, he had no baby on hand with which to soothe President Bush and stop him biting him. Henry and John's likely cortisol-addled brains also led them to behave in ways that further deepened the chasm of status between them and their American hosts.

Do these studies of the effects of stress, then, point to the answer to the riddle of the Oscars and the mystery of the Glasgow graveyards? Encounters of low-status individuals with high-status ones can be very stressful, and stress triggers cortisol. Cortisol in the short term is usefully energising, but when chronically secreted into the blood over the long term, it can have very damaging effects on the body, including the cardiovascular system.[10] Chronic high levels of cortisol also shrink cells in certain areas of the brain.

Were the successful Oscar nominees, the Nobel Prize winners and the merchants whose families could afford the bigger gravestones simply like dominant baboons whose bodies have been protected by their status from the long-term corrosive effects of cortisol, which less successful, lower-status individuals suffered, triggered by the repeated stress of encountering higher-status peers? Maybe. But there is a problem. Why did other British politicians who passed under Sir Christopher's judging eyes not succumb to this apparently evolutionarily predestined status stress? Michael Marmot and his colleagues from University

College London have shown that higher-ranking civil servants live longer and have less illness than lower ranking ones, irrespective of the health of their lifestyles.[11] Why is there such a difference in survival rates between civil servants of the same rank? And why do politicians who are high on the status ladder in their own countries respond so strongly to someone of even higher status from elsewhere?

Is the answer to the mystery of the Oscars a simple question of their place in the status hierarchy? Not fully: while the higher-status, 'dominant-baboon effect' of the Academy Award winner may be part of the solution to the mystery of the Oscars, it does not fully explain the puzzle because the status that wealthy and famous film-star nominees have is so high anyway that it is difficult to believe that an Oscar could increase their status by such an enormous amount as to give them four extra years of life on average. If status on its own does not solve the mystery of the Oscars, is there another ingredient in the Oscar elixir? To answer this question, consider the following scenario.

Genghis Khan and the typists

It was the antediluvian, pre-desktop-computer age of 1979. I gave the psychology department secretary Linda my handwritten report. She looked harassed as she took it, pulling some papers from the mound on her desk.

'Here's your last report, Ian,' she said, handing me my previous report. 'I hope there aren't too many mistakes. I don't really have enough time to correct them . . . and my Tippex is nearly out.'

She gave me a wan smile, hauled back the typewriter carriage and began to type, fast and ferocious, shoulders hunched over the clack-clacking machine.

'Damn! The ribbon's out.' The type had faded on the page. She rummaged in her drawer, found a new ribbon, ripped out the old one and pressed the new reel into place. She cursed softly as she threaded it into the empty receiving reel and finally stood up, holding up her blackened fingers for me to see.

'This stuff never comes out, and look at that pile – it's never-ending.' With a sigh she headed off to wash her hands.

Clare's door was opened as I passed. She was the other secretary in the department, and did the typing for some of the other psychologists. She was applying varnish to a fingernail. I stuck my head round the door.

'Don't suppose you could make a few corrections on this report, Clare?'

She looked up with a bright smile.

'Sorry, Ian, got a lot on – best if Linda corrects her own.'

'She's pretty busy . . .'

The smile snapped off.

'So am I,' she said, her eyes flicking in the direction of a single report sitting on her empty desk.

I went to say something, realised there was no point, and moved off. I would find some of my own Tippex and use a black pen to hand-write the corrections on to the white paste once it had dried. That's what the psychologists that Clare was working for often did anyway.

Linda and Clare were secretaries on the same grade. But Linda was over-burdened and harassed, while Clare was relaxed and serene. They had the same status, but seemed to be reacting differently to their roles.

*   *   *

Among many of the baboon species of Africa, the high-status male baboons have an easier time selecting their sexual partners – hardly surprising given the stress that they cause to low-status baboons when they bump into them. Evolutionary justice, we might think – the dominant males passing on their genes in greater numbers than their stressed and wary low-status troop members.

This alpha-male sex fest is just as strong in we humans as it is in the other primates. Take Tom Robinson, a mild-mannered accountant who lives in Miami, Florida. His great, great-grandfather was Genghis Khan. He knows this because in his genes is a Y chromosome which can be traced back to an extraordinary prolific individual who lived in Central Asia around AD 1200[12]. As this person is the great-to-the-power-of-forty grandfather of roughly one in twelve of all Asian men (and an unknown proportion of women who do not have Y chromosomes), it can be safely assumed that the great Mongol emperor Genghis Khan had a fairly active love life, for which his genes should be very grateful.

Genghis Khan was absolute ruler of the biggest contiguous empire in history, which spread at times from the Sea of Japan in the east to the outskirts of Vienna in the west. He had six Mongolian wives, but during his conquests he also married many daughters of foreign kings who were smart enough to submit to his rule. What's more, whenever a territory was conquered, the mass rape of women could not begin until the most beautiful women had been selected and sent to the emperor for his pleasure.

An Irish equivalent of Genghis Khan has been identified by Dan Bradley, one of my colleagues at Trinity College Dublin, and his research team. Dan is an extremely clever, modest and mild-mannered geneticist who has a strong interest in a fabled Irish warrior, the greatest High King of Ireland, Niall of the Nine Hostages.[13] Niall was a warlord of the fifth century whose stronghold was in the north-west of Ireland, from where he sent many invading foreign armies back to their boats. He also had a penchant for violent incursions on his neighbours, with all that this entails. Niall's dynasty maintained their power for an extraordinary period – right up until Trinity College Dublin's founder, Queen Elizabeth I of England, finally crushed the dominance of the ancient Irish nobility at the end of the sixteenth century.

From Bradley's research, it looks as though Niall was quite literally one of the fathers of his nation – a man who, 1,500 years after his death, has up to three million living descendants in Ireland and elsewhere. St Columba of Iona was reputedly the great-great-grandson of Niall. Around one in twelve men in Ireland are descended from him – including the mild-mannered Dan Bradley, now known by some of his Trinity colleagues as Genghis Dan.

Genghis Khan, Niall of the Nine Hostages and the top baboons all had vigorous sex lives and the first choice of the most desirable females in their tribes and troops. For their male underlings, life – and, in particular, sexual and family life – would have been challenging and limited because of the alpha-male dominance over the available females and the punishment awaiting more junior males should they rashly decide to compete for the females.

Actually the lower-status baboons have found a clever way of passing on their genes that no doubt some of Genghis and Niall's courtiers and servants also cottoned on to. In the 1994 Quentin

Tarantino movie *Pulp Fiction*, the junior gangster played by John Travolta is told to look after the psychopathic gang boss's wife for the evening. Stressed out though he is, he begins to yield as she ruthlessly deploys her seductive looks and boss's-moll status on him. Exactly this scenario plays out in baboon troops, where females choose lower-status males for platonic relationships that involve mutual grooming – roughly the equivalent of the hamburger and slow dancing of Travolta's and Uma Thurman's characters. Many of the junior males who are selected by the females for this sort of friendship end up – as Travolta's character might have done with Thurman's had the latter not overdosed on the former's heroin – in the baboon equivalent of bed with their female paramours.

The low-dominance baboons therefore manage to escape the monopoly on mates that the higher-ranking animals try to impose by this subtle exercise of control behind the scenes. Interestingly, these low-status males also show much less evidence of stress, and the bodily wear and tear associated with it, than do their low-status peers who have not learned this trick.

So what has all this got to do with Linda, Clare and the typing dramas of a 1970s university psychology department? Linda and Clare were both relatively lower in the social hierarchy of the department than the professional staff, and we can confidently predict from Michael Marmot's research[14] that over the next four or five decades they would more likely have ended up being sicker than the psychologists for whom they typed.

But while Linda was clearly showing the signs of stress that are associated with such low-status jobs, Clare seemed to be under much less pressure. Why? Each had the same workload and the same status, but Clare had one striking advantage – *control*. Clare was able to exert control over the timing and flow of her work. She agreed to do certain tasks, but not others. As a result, her desk was not piled high with uncompleted work and she had control over her working day. Linda, on the other hand, felt constantly swamped by her work and, for whatever reason, did not have control over it.

So, like the low-ranking baboons who managed to have control over their sex lives by making initially platonic friendships with the dominant baboons' mates, Clare was able to control her workload through various interpersonal strategies and hence avoid one of the toxic elements of low status – *loss of control.*

I did not measure Linda and Clare's blood pressure, pulse rate or blood cortisol levels at the time, but I would bet handsomely on Linda showing a lot more signs of stress-related wear and tear than Clare. This was true of the low-status baboons who made friends with the females, and it is also true of civil servants who are on the same objective grade: those who have more day-to-day control over the timing and rate of their work, irrespective of job title, have lower blood pressure than their colleagues of the same status who have less control. Given the cost of health care for corporations, and the loss of productivity that illness causes, even small changes in how much control employees *feel* over their workplace could have greater health and hence financial benefits for an organisation than all the healthy lifestyle programmes put together.

Martin Seligman, in 1972, famously studied the effects of identical amounts of stress – in the form of electric shocks – on two groups of animals under conditions where the shock could be terminated by jumping over a low barrier, versus when it was delivered randomly and nothing could be done about it.[15] Even though the amounts of shock given to the two groups were identical, the no-control stress group ended up suffering from what Seligman called 'learned helplessness' – a state of apathy,

depression and anxiety which meant that even when they subsequently could escape from shock, they failed to do so.

So was Linda in a situation of learned helplessness – feeling
constantly overwhelmed by work that she could not control – in
contrast to Clare, who had the same workload but was relatively
unstressed because she could influence its flow? Is the amount of
control we have over our lives the secret of longevity?

Do we have the solution to the mystery of the Oscars? Does
winning an Oscar or a Nobel Prize give us more control over our
lives, and hence make us more invulnerable to stress and its toxic
effects? Yes, but still we are not quite there: how do we explain
Linda's and Clare's different responses to roughly the same working
environment? Objectively, both had approximately the same level
of control over their daily working lives, yet Linda was the one who
felt stressed and overwhelmed by the demands we made on her.

And anyway, the average Oscar nominee who never actually
gets to walk up the red carpet and accept the statuette has buck-
ets of control over his or her life. Does getting the award really
make that much difference to how much they can call the shots
in an already very privileged and self-determined life?

So yes, control is important, but there is something missing
in trying to work out why the Oscar has such incredible medical
properties and to find out what it is, we must travel back in time
to a war zone.

Survival, evasion, resistance, escape

It was 26 October 1967. There was a blaze of lights on the plane's
control panel and an electronic howl of warning telling the pilot
that missile radar had locked on to his A-4E Skyhawk fighter.

The Yen Phu power station in central Hanoi mushroomed towards him and at 3,000 feet he released his bombs, just as the cloud of smoke from the missile battery spat the shining capsule of high explosive towards him, blowing off his right wing and hurling him out into the sky. That was the last John McCain saw of the inside of a plane until he prepared for his flight back home on 14 March 1973.

When McCain was captured he was not treated at the infamous 'Hanoi Hilton' POW compound – he was left to die of his injuries until the Viet Cong discovered that his father was an admiral, and soon to be head of the entire Pacific Command. In his 1995 book *The Nightingale's Song*, Robert Timberg describes the broken, filthy and emaciated figure that was carried into the cockroach-infested cell in another POW centre, known as the Plantation. Such was his state, his two cellmates believed he would not survive the night. That was until they saw the strange and feverish light of his saucer eyes – a blaze of raw vitality that had him talking into the darkness until he fell asleep at 3 a.m.

McCain had had to offer some military information to get treatment for his severe injuries, otherwise he would certainly have died, so he signed one 'confession' statement. But when, in 1968, he was offered release, he refused with a torrent of ripe insults at the very senior American officials who had come to try to secure the return of a son of the elite. Their success would have served to demoralise hundreds of thousands of US servicemen who were already all too aware that most of the well-educated and the rich had avoided serving in Vietnam.

McCain's refusal of release must have been all the harder when the cellmate who had nursed him back to life accepted freedom. McCain was to suffer another five years as a POW, much of it in solitary confinement.

In 1968, the Viet Cong were using torture and 'mind-control' methods very similar to those used by the Communist forces in Korea more than a decade earlier. During the Korean War of the early 1950s, mind-control methods had been put into operation, which had resulted in seemingly brainwashed captured US servicemen appearing on television condemning US capitalism and praising the wonders of Communism. How was it that young American servicemen could appear to praise a political system that was so alien to their own upbringing and education? How were they so apparently successfully brainwashed?

To try to understand this phenomenon, and at the same time to try to find methods to inoculate captured US forces against its effects, the US military began to adopt significant elements of the south-east Asian methods to train their own forces how to resist if they were taken prisoner.

The Survival, Evasion, Resistance and Escape program – SERE – has been used for decades to train US service personnel in these techniques. SERE includes solitary confinement, sensory deprivation, constant noise, sudden and disorienting violence, sleep deprivation, forced maintenance of 'stress positions' and – in a small number of cases – water-boarding.

If that list looks familiar, that is because the SERE programme is the basis for the procedures used at Guantánamo Bay, Abu Ghraib and the CIA 'Black Sites' in Poland, Romania and elsewhere in the aftermath of 9/11. The images that first appeared in 2002 from Guantánamo Bay of orange-suited detainees in hoods, ear-muffs, outlandish goggles, thick mittens and constraining chains shuffling out into the stifling Cuban heat for 'exercise' were bizarre. But all these items were being used for a purpose: to cut out as much sensory input to the brain as possible – an experience that can cause severe disorientation and psychotic-like symptoms, including hallucinations, paralysing anxiety and much more.

Yet here is the problem that the US generals wrestled with: why do some people succumb to this treatment while others do not? If they could answer that, then they could protect against it. Eventually they found at least a partial answer, and it lies in a declassified secret report by military psychology researchers which had been written in 1978.[16]

The sunny coastline of San Diego can blow cooling air from the Pacific on to the baking heat of summer, and the 'June Gloom' can even bring a chilling mist more reminiscent of San Francisco than southern California to tame the heat. But these remissions apart, the oven-heat of the city's summer can be brutal. That's why the servicemen and women assigned to the US Navy's Survival, Evasion, Resistance and Escape School in San Diego experience a particular dread during the summer months. They know that the heat will magnify the physical and mental pain they are about to experience in the horribly realistic simulated POW camp.

The SERE experience causes dizzyingly high levels of the stress hormone cortisol in the blood of those who have endured it at the end of these courses. And under these stress levels, some people break and divulge more information than the basic minimum the military code of conduct demands they reveal as prisoners of war. So, *who breaks and why?*

The 1978 document answers that question. But it also goes some way to solving the mystery of the Oscars and explaining the obelisks of Glasgow, Henry McLeish's star-struck incoherence and Linda's and Clare's different work experiences.

Take a moment to answer these questions to get an idea of how likely you would be to break after a SERE experience. Circle 5 for 'agree strongly', 0 for 'totally disagree'.

1. People earn the respect they are due in the long run.

   0 1 2 3 4 5

2. Most people don't realise how much they control their own fate.

   0 1 2 3 4 5

3. How hard I work is the main determinant of my exam results.

   0 1 2 3 4 5

4. Persist long and hard enough and your assets will be recognised.

   0 1 2 3 4 5

5. The little guy can have an impact on the world, not just the power holders.

   0 1 2 3 4 5

6. Our lives are shaped largely by forces we don't understand and can't control.

   0 1 2 3 4 5

7. Don't plan too far ahead because chance will largely shape your fate.

   0 1 2 3 4 5

8. Mostly I can't work out why politicians do the things they do.

   0 1 2 3 4 5

9. Often exam questions are so unrelated to the course work that it is pointless studying.

   0 1 2 3 4 5

10. To get a good job, it's mainly a question of being in the right place at the right time.

    0 1 2 3 4 5

These questions are similar to those derived from research by the great American psychologist Julian Rotter, of the University of

Connecticut, and developed by Barry Collins at the University of California at Los Angeles.[17]

Now add up your scores for the first five questions – the maximum is 25 and the minimum is 0.

Next add up your scores for the last five questions – the maximum again is 25 and the minimum 0.

The higher service personnel scored on questions like 1–5 and the lower they scored on questions similar to 6–10, the less likely they were to break. In other words, if for example they scored 25 for the former and 0 for the latter, then they would be among the least likely to have buckled under the SERE programme. If on the other hand they scored 0 for the first five and 25 for the last five questions, they would have been much more likely to have yielded to the intense mental and physical pressures of the regime.

But why should answers to questions about such things as school grades and politics have anything to do with breaking under torture? The answer to this question is key not only to how we are likely to respond to torture and mind control, it may also contribute to explaining the Oscars mystery. The answer lies in our belief that we have control.

Linda did not have much control over her workload, while Clare did. The low-status baboons who would otherwise have been stressed and prone to illness managed to gain some surreptitious levels of control by befriending the females of the senior baboons. But in John McCain's case, as in the case of those SERE trainees who managed to resist interrogation and torture, the key was not actual control, but rather their *belief* that they had control over their lives in general.

The military psychologists of the San Diego SERE training school pinpointed in these questions a psychological orientation to the world which teased out how much people felt in control of their own fate. It was this sense of control that McCain's cell-mates saw blazing out of the eyes of an otherwise broken body.

So regimes like Vietnam POW interrogation centres, Abu Ghraib and Guantánamo Bay break some prisoners but not others. And this means not just in spirit or body, but in the very tissue of their brains. Brain cells shrink under the shock of super-high doses of cortisol induced by the torture process, which are poisonous to the brain at high levels and the birth of new brain cells in the memory centres is curtailed. But how is it that some brains shrink and others do not?

The answer was found 2,000 miles north-east of San Diego in Montreal, where researchers were puzzled by this question. A research team at the Montreal Neurological Institute stressed their volunteers by giving them difficult mental arithmetic to do under timed pressure while undergoing brain scans and receiving critical comments about their performance from the researchers. This is indeed a pretty stressful situation to be in, and all the physiological measurements taken by the team confirmed that.[18]

Just as the San Diego SERE trainees divided into those who broke and those who did not, so the Montreal research volunteers varied in how stressed they were in the mental-arithmetic-with-criticism test. The researchers measured their stress by how much cortisol was pumped into their bloodstream: one group triggered a lot more than the other. Who were they? The answer was those who generally felt less in control of their lives.

So what? We all know that some people get more stressed by exams, criticism and work difficulties than others. Some human beings are just plain nervy, aren't they? Here's why it is relevant: the Montreal researchers found that there was a strong linkage between the size of the memory centre in their volunteers' brains – the hippocampus – and how much they felt they had an internal control over their lives, as measured by a questionnaire similar to the one you answered above.

No one can avoid stress in today's business world, and some organisations, by the very nature of their business, demand long hours and pressing deadlines. Stress takes its toll on the brain and body, but the problem is that men and women in the organisation may look good on the outside, but inside, important brain centres are being corroded by the damaging chemicals that prolonged stress triggers. For key individuals in an organisation to be suffering from impaired memory and reduced problem-solving and planning ability represents an enormous risk. The lessons from Montreal are that we can perhaps protect people from the worst, invisible effects of stress by building as much control as possible into their working lives, even if we cannot alter the objective levels of work or the harshness of the deadlines.

Belief that you have control, then, is like an antidote to stress – a sort of anti-viral drug against the mutant virus of psychological strain. With a sense of internal control over events in life, our bodies will pump less cortisol into our bloodstreams. Over a lifetime, our brains and bodies will therefore be spared repeated overdoses of a potent hormone that in high doses shrinks brain cells and their connections, particularly in the brain's highly sensitive memory centres.

So is this the final answer to the mystery of the Oscars? Does winning an Oscar, or a Nobel Prize, somehow boost a belief that you have control over your life and so protects you from the ravages of stress? Is control something that goes hand in hand with status – lengthening the lives and replenishing the pockets of those whose families built the biggest towers over their graves in Glasgow? Did Clare the typist have leverage over her workload because she believed she had control more generally, and hence acted in order to create that control in reality? Do managers live longer and healthier lives because they hold the reins of power in the organisation precisely because their self-belief in their ability to control events has had them promoted? Is it this key belief in control that shapes our lives and careers, wherever we are in the pecking order?

Is the Oscar puzzle solved, then? Winners live longer because it strengthens their belief that they have control in the world and this belief inoculates them against the corrosive effects of stress on their bodies? Yes, but there is something not quite sufficient about this explanation. To discover what is missing from this promising but incomplete answer, we should consider some events that took place in twelfth-century France.

The psychological Crusade

On 31 March 1146, Bernard of Clairvaux, the leading figure of the Cistercian Order, made a speech in the French town of Vézelay, an oration commissioned by the Pope and given in the presence of King Louis VII of France. It was important because Christian Europe was reeling from the recent massacres and defeat of the First Crusade at the Siege of Edessa. Bernard was one of the first evangelists of the self. And in this speech he roused an enormous crowd to zealous action, as they discarded their tools and left their homes to march off towards the heat and carnage of the Middle East. How had he energised a sullen, war-resistant peasantry? He had done so by promising a new type of spiritual redemption: the salvation of the individual as opposed to the collective soul.

Bernard's Eastertide speech was a call to war. It was also a recruitment drive for the Second Crusade, but it was a difficult pitch for him to make – there was very little appetite for more war, at least among the weary peasants of Christendom, by contrast with its warlike knights. And this was one of the reasons why Pope Eugenius III had called for Bernard's help. For the monk was not only a mesmerising and fiery preacher, he was also in the vanguard of a fundamental reshaping of the human mind in the Christian world. This reshaping continues to have its effect on our minds and brains to this very day.

What was this shift in human psychology? The biblical prophecy that humanity's Last Days would culminate in a spiritual redemption coinciding with the second coming of Jesus Christ was as real and vivid to people then as the landing on the moon or the Hiroshima bomb is to us today. These theological precepts were not woolly, abstract ideas – they were vivid and terrifying realities by which people lived and died.

But there was one crucial difference in the nature of these realities leading up to the time of St Bernard, and what followed afterwards, as the great social psychologist Roy Baumeister of Florida State University pointed out in the seminal paper 'How the Self Became a Problem: A Psychological Review of Historical Research'.[19] Undoubtedly this shift in psychology was not a clear, sudden change caused by one man but, as Professor Colin Morris of the University of Oxford has shown, St Bernard was a particularly important node in the wrenching psychological and social changes that were happening at that time.

So what was this dizzying swerve in the history of human consciousness that happened around the time of St Bernard? The answer is in the title of Morris's book, *The Discovery of the Individual, 1050–1200*. In Christian theology, the Messiah, Jesus Christ, will return to earth for the Last Judgement, when, in an apocalyptic convulsion, believers in Christ will be 'saved' – transported to heaven – and non-believers will be abandoned to their fate. Until the time of St Bernard, according to Morris, who was saved and who was not was more or less a matter of church membership: just being a member of the 'universal church' guaranteed a ticket to spiritual salvation. Being saved, in other words, was a collective rather than an individual phenomenon. According to these beliefs, the individual person was not a major focus of attention. In fact, classical Greece, in whose philosophy and language Christianity has many of its origins, did not even have a word for the modern sense of 'person', Morris says; the nearest word can be crudely translated as 'substance'.

Spiritual salvation, then, was pretty much a matter of theological accountancy until this time – a largely external system of discipline, penances and indulgences. But as the twelfth century progressed, old certainties were beginning to break down. Rules which previously had been believed to be immutable, eternal and God-given – for instance about the correct way for knights or monks to behave – began to be interpreted and reformulated in slightly different versions by various groups and authorities. Consensus began to crumble around the edges, and competing versions of how to achieve salvation began to be generated.

It was as if a pearl necklace had broken and the individual pearls had scattered across the floor, no longer held together by the string. There were many possible ways in which the pearls could now be arranged – competing necklaces to which they could be attached. But which one to choose?

Suddenly there was choice among different voices of authority. No longer could you get through life on the unselfconscious path of a solid, single and accepted reality. Now there were competing realities, rules that vied with one another. How does the human mind cope with this? It copes in the same way that a child torn between rowing parents deals with it – it turns inside, to the individual self of an interior world, and St Bernard was the psychologist who helped the child cope in this way.

Bernard's therapy was the 'taking of the cross', whereby pilgrims made crosses out of wood or cloth to hold up as symbols of their holy engagement – and as a powerful, individual means of gaining absolution and holy grace. The crowd flocked to Bernard with their crosses: he reputedly gave up his outer coat for more crosses to be made from it. Bernard wrote to the Pope some time afterwards, telling him that whole cities and castles were nearly emptied, with only one man left for every seven women. And unlike in the First Crusade, European royalty joined this one, not only for political and economic reasons, but also impelled by the feverish excitement of the possibility of a new, improved – and above all, individual – salvation.

Pilgrimages such as the one to Santiago de Compostela in Spain really took off at this time, according to Morris. By these journeys, the citizens of Europe who were losing their old certainties sought to re-establish some version of them – in the discovered truths of an outward and inner journey. This new focus on the interior self was mirrored in art, where artists began to move away from the stylised icon to the flesh and blood of the individualised painted portrait. Around this time writers and performers also rediscovered the satire of the classical world – the sardonic mocking of received wisdoms which served to further distance people from the hitherto blindly accepted truths of an unquestioned existence.

Of course the individual self existed before 1146 and the collective self continued long after. But the journey inwards was accelerated after this time, with another milestone in the history of self appearing in the form of Martin Luther and the Reformation four centuries later. The Reformation challenged the Church at the highest level and the resulting convulsions gave another turbo-charged boost to the idea of the individual. The rise of Protestantism spawned a world-changing epidemic of individual conscience, self-examination and personal responsibility.

But even the new Protestants did not unchain the individual self: the Pilgrim Fathers may have demanded ruthless self-examination, but the new self that they had bred was kept carefully caged in the strictness of observance and social and religious conformity. Yes, the individual now had to wrestle with biblical truth in a way that the early-twelfth-century citizen did not, but this was still no unfettered hippy self of the 1960s.

That sixties ego was another historical milestone in the history of self. Never before had ordinary people felt quite so liberated from any rules; never previously had they been able to pick and choose their identity. We now saw a new type of pilgrimage, but this time not to holy sanctuaries like Santiago de Compostela, but rather an interior journey into one's own head in search of that elusive – and now made holy – self.

When, during the 1970s, the 2003 Nobel Prize winners for medicine Peter Mansfield and Paul Lauterbur invented Magnetic Resonance Imaging (MRI), a way of looking inside the body and brain using huge magnetic fields, they could not have imagined that one day it would be used to dissect the anatomy of that self which St Bernard had help liberate more than eight hundred years earlier. Magnetic Resonance Imaging eventually gave rise to *functional* MRI (fMRI), which during the 1990s transformed the study of human psychology by allowing scientists to see the physical workings of the brain that underpin mental life. For the first time, a key was turned in the lock of personal subjectivity.

Along with memory, emotion, reasoning and attention, researchers began to probe for that elusive beast – the individual self – in the soft, pulsing tissue of the brain. Appropriately enough in the light of the internal journeys upon which Bernard, Luther and Timothy Leary sent millions of young Westerners, the self was indeed partly 'inside' the brain. Lying in the noisy tunnel of the MRI scanner during the typical experiment on self-scrutiny, participants would be asked to think about themselves and answer questions such as 'Would you describe yourself as outgoing?' and 'Are you an anxious person?' They made these judgements about public figures as well, and the activity in their brains was traced.

When we are prompted to this type of self-examination, the inside surface of the front part of our brains becomes very active. Behind the forehead, the two halves of the brain curve back into themselves and it is these inside surfaces of the cortex which are part of the brain's network for self-scrutiny. But there is a further division of labour within this interior strip of the brain: the bottom section – the ventro-medial prefrontal cortex – tends to be where our really personal, subjective thinking about ourselves goes on. This area is very strongly connected to the brain's emotional centres.

Above this part of the brain – in the dorso-medial prefrontal cortex – seems to be the region where self-examination meets the outside world. While its neighbour underneath is more connected to the emotional regions of the brain, this upstairs self-area is more strongly linked to the outside surfaces of the brain where thinking, planning and judging take place. This upper self-area is where we make comparisons between ourselves and other people and things; it is also the area of the brain where we think and empathise about what is going on in other people's minds.

When we ask secular citizens of the post-war 'baby boomer' generation to think about themselves and their traits, we see the usual inside-surface brain activity of the middle of the frontal lobe, but particularly located in the emotion-linked lower part. But what happens when the descendants of Bernard and Luther think about themselves? Bernard and Luther may have helped liberate the cog of self from the great wheel of orthodoxy but, when they are compared with the non-religious self-focused children of the late twentieth and early twenty-first centuries, we can assume – but not prove – that at least some of today's practising Christians still have an identity that is embedded within what they see as a bigger, transcendent reality. And Professor Shihui Han of Beijing University has provided an intriguing test of whether historical religious belief may be expressed in the brains of today's believers.[20] Studying Chinese Christians, and comparing them with non-believers, he discovered that believers show a quite different pattern of brain activation.

Han found that Christians activated the dorsal – the upper – part of the middle surface of the frontal lobes when thinking about themselves, much more than the emotionally linked ventral parts. In other words, their self-reflection was more tied in to the external world and to other people's minds than self-reflection was in non-believers. More specifically, when they thought about themselves, it appears that they may have been thinking about how Jesus would judge them. How can we say this? Because the amount of activity in this upper part of the brain region was strongly related to how important the participants rated Jesus's judgement in subjective evaluation of a person's personality. Bernard's theology, then – the belief that an individual could take steps to achieve his or her own salvation – appears as a ghostly glimmer in the brains of these Chinese Christian students whose sense of individual self, unlike that of their secular peers, appeared to be shaped by a sense of being watched or judged by the source of their hoped-for individual salvation.

But how does this help us with the Oscars mystery? How does the medieval realisation of the individual self explain how a sense of control boosted by winning an Oscar might lengthen life? Having a sense of control is incredibly important, as we saw earlier. But here is the issue – control *by whom*? If we are cogs in the wheel of destiny, then our freedom of action and control in the world is pretty limited, unless we are oligarchs or politically empowered national leaders.

But once we become freelance individuals making our way in the world, we may feel in control. Many people running small businesses will gladly work eighty hours per week for less money than they would earn in a big corporation, simply to have that sense of control over their own destiny. But we might well also begin to feel something in addition to this heady freedom. And that something, its roots deep in the soil of the twelfth century, may help us explain why control is such an important – but partial – answer to the Oscars Mystery.

'Me' is a lonely place, and the flipside of its freedom is its isolated vulnerability, particularly in a secular world. We've seen that a sense of control is crucial for survival. Could it be that control's special place in helping people live longer has something to do with St Bernard's individual self and its search for salvation? If a sense of control makes Oscar winners live longer, what exactly is this life-lengthening something that they are controlling?

They only knew him as Null Achtzehn – German for Zero-Eighteen. No one knew his name. He may have forgotten it himself and anyway he did not really exist any more. When he spoke or looked around, he gave the impression of being quite empty inside. Null Achtzehn was young and by no means the weakest of the work party, but in spite of that everyone tried to avoid working with him.

They stayed away from him because of his terrifying indifference. He was so apathetic that he did not even bother to avoid blows, preserve his strength or search for food. He did everything he was told with total indifference, to the point that from time to time, without warning, he would simply drop like a stone to the ground with an exhaustion he had not bothered to fight off. When his time came, Null Achtzehn obediently shuffled off to the extermination chamber with that same awful indifference.

Primo Levi, in his harrowing account of Auschwitz *If This Is a Man*, knew well the warning signs of fellow inmates giving up on the struggle for survival of their selves – and Null Achtzehn was one of these described in this book. Levi observed that when inmates of the camp gave up on their personhood under the soul-crushing regime of the concentration camp they soon died, as the young Null Achtzehn did not long after.

Levi also used to watch the Greeks at the Auschwitz market – a forbidden corner of the camp where crusts of bread and half-cups of soup were traded – silent and motionless like sphinxes. The Greeks from the Jewish colony of Salonica sat there with their bowls of thick potage, not the dirty water that passed for soup in the rest of the camp. These were the fruits of their solidarity and co-operation, which had allowed them to seize the key prisoner posts in the camp and become the monopoly traders of the hunger market. This sense of community preserved and protected not just their bodies – but the very core of their humanity, that precious, individual *self*. Whereas, even if they avoided the extermination chambers, the many who, like Null Achtzehn, gave up on that individuality and the self-respect that went with it, soon died in the camp of . . . what? Despair? Depression? Or is there some selfhood whose health and survival is as essential to life as a beating heart? Was it the failure of this organ that actually killed Null Achtzehn?

The worst sort of stress

One day Professor Sally Dickerson of the University of California at Irvine asked a very important question:[21] what stresses us most? Is it financial insecurity? Worries about our health? Work strains and pressure? Fear of death? Concern about our children? Fear of burglary or attack? Phobias? Too many demands on our time?

Yes, these are all major sources of stress, but there was one particular type of stress that, life-threatening trauma for you or your family apart, could raise cortisol levels more than any other. I was brought up in a 'council flat' rented from the local authority. My father had for the times a good, steady job, as an electrician in an engineering factory, but we did not have enough money for a car or luxuries.

The fact of my living in such an apartment is important because many of my school friends lived in relatively spacious, middle-class housing and their fathers had cars. My dad, on the other hand, rode a bicycle to work. As adolescence approached, I began to feel ashamed of where I lived. While this feeling – essentially a sense of social inferiority – disappeared as I grew up, I was shocked to find its sudden re-emergence a few years later, after I had left home. I was back in Glasgow for a conference and staying with my parents for the night. A well-known local psychiatrist kindly offered to drive me home. I am ashamed to admit that I had him drop me off on the main road a quarter of a mile from my home, so that he would not see where I had been brought up. I remember him looking at me as he drove off, clearly aware that I was not going into the house where he had dropped me.

I did not know it then, but the emotions I was feeling were ones produced by what Dickerson has found to be the most widespread and potent form of stress for human beings – *social-evaluative threat*, or SET. Now, in my case, this threat was very mild and largely in my mind, and was certainly not an acute stressor, particularly once I was a reasonably performing young adult making my way in the world.

At the heart of this feeling of shame is a belief that others will judge who you are – your self – as inferior or inadequate. Shame is an ancient evolved emotion that Charles Darwin described as relating almost exclusively to the judgement of others.

Take baboons, for instance. One of the most stressful things that can happen to a baboon, as measured by cortisol levels in the blood, is to have his social status lowered by defeat or subordination by another baboon. It is the same for humans. For many of us – Henry McLeish would be one example for whom this was the case – encountering a higher-status dominant individual can convey a sense of threat and shame.

In all animals, including humans, social threat has big effects on the immune system. When this feeling of being looked down upon or rejected by others persists over time, it can impact our health. It is this sense of social rejection that, for instance, makes redundancy so particularly painful, irrespective of the financial compensation. A study by Steve Cole and colleagues from the University of California at Los Angeles studied the progress of HIV-infected people.[22] They found that those who were particularly sensitive to feeling rejected by others because of their homosexuality showed greater declines over the next nine years in their immune function, particularly in a type of immune system cell called the CD4 T-cell, than the ones who cared less about rejection by other people. These self-threatened people developed AIDS and died around two years sooner than those with a more secure and less threatened homosexual identity.

Given that these two groups of HIV-infected gay men were healthy at the start of the study, and were not different on any physical, social or psychological measures at the beginning of the nine-year period, this suggests that the threats to self that come from feeling that others think badly of you and reject you because of some aspect of your identity may indeed be toxic and damaging to health. These were not general effects of unhappiness or low psychological state. How do we know this? Because whereas feeling rejected by other people is strongly linked to the immune system health as measured by CD4 T-cell levels – sadness, anxiety, general stress and depression are *not*, Sally Dickerson and her colleagues at the University of Irvine have found.[23]

When Bernard of Clairvaux helped free the individual, interior selves of pre-Renaissance Europeans from their previously relatively unselfconscious communal selves, it had both benefits and costs. The benefits included the flowering of individual creativity and free thought, culminating eventually in the birth of science and the modern world. But the costs included the creation of a vulnerable, threat-prone individual self liable to *shame*. What is shame? It is the re-creation inside one's own head of the negative judgements of other people.

Think of a time when you have done something shameful. What does it feel like? You think things like, 'I want to hide', you want to crouch down, shrink away from other people, lower your eyes, and so on. These are all ancient tokens of submission – of yielding to a superior. And they are very like the signs of submission that other primates show when they yield to a more dominant animal: they imply that you are withdrawing, and disengaging.

In evolutionary history, these signals can help us survive by showing our competitors that we are not going to compete

– directly at least – for resources or mates. Allowing the boss to feel dominant by a display of deference on our part can be an important way of reintroducing harmony to the office: throughout evolutionary history, submission displays, of which shame is one, have served the important functions of keeping the group together and avoiding too much wasteful conflict.

Because we are a group animal, we have inherited strong needs for acceptance by others because without friends we would be more readily excluded from the group and fall victim to animals or other groups of humans. To live in a group with other people demands that I try to read their minds. I have to try to work out what they think and feel about me – otherwise, how can I know whether I am accepted or not? That means I have to create images – representations – of other people's minds in my own mind. The best businesses and corporations manage to create cultures which make it easier for employees and managers to 'read' one another because of feeling part of that culture.

But it is not other people's minds in general that I create images of – it is their reactions to *me* that I store so that I can navigate the politics, intrigues, loyalties and betrayals of the group. In doing this, I have to create a 'me' image that is at the centre of this mental school playground. In fact, the 'me' that develops is essentially the sum of my images of what all these other minds think and feel about me. The great American sociologist George Herbert Mead most famously developed this idea of 'me' as a magical mirror reflecting the minds of others.

In Christendom before 1150 that 'me' was securely chiselled into a solid and infinite reality of divine fate. My place in the world was pretty much a manifestation of God's will and the really important thing about my life – my soul's avoidance of eternal damnation – was a group thing: if the Church got it right, then we'd all be OK. From the mid-thirteenth century, and then again in the Reformation, but most spectacularly in the second half of the twentieth century, however, that 'me' progressively broke off from the granite rock of infinity. No longer was 'me' securely fastened within the mind of God. Come the twenty-first century, 'me' is no longer always even fastened within the mind of a group of people – community, extended family, or even nuclear family. No longer is there a stable group of people in whose mirror gaze one's self is fixed. Instead, we move about, often from relationship to relationship, and the sustenance of that 'me', which is the sum of other people's views of me, becomes something I have to actively manage and manipulate myself.

Along with the sense of liberation that can surely go with this – what small-town adolescent has not craved escape from the claustrophobic twenty-four-hour scrutiny of the community? – comes that vulnerability of the 'me', constantly threatened with change in the shifting reflecting mirrors of passing minds in a changing social world.

What else can we do in such turmoil but to create defences – to build self-esteem as a protection against the threat? But that self-esteem can be fragile and threats to the vulnerable, exposed self, stripped of its secure place in a group mind, are thus among the most stressful experiences that we can have as human beings. What's more, these threats are magnified further the less control we have over them. When it comes to the puzzle of the Oscars, I have already showed that having control – but more impor-tantly, feeling in control – is a potential reason why the Oscar winners live so much longer than nominees.

But when it comes to the question of control for what reason, St Bernard has given us a possible answer – the reason we seek control so much, and why it is so good for our mental and phys-ical health, is that control allows me to protect my self. If I am a small contributing part of a single greater reality, then my self is less exposed and threatened: the greater reality of the big wheel will keep on turning without me, and so, in a sense, my self continues insofar as the greater reality continues. As a small part of a greater reality, my individual self is less exposed to threat. While the notion of lifetime loyalty to corporations in the Japanese mode is probably no longer tenable in the globalised world, there are enormous potential benefits in trying to foster work cultures where individuals feel part of a greater project at a personal level.

But if my self has gone it alone as an existential sole trader, then 'I' am all I have. And the greatest threat to that 'I' comes from the judgement and acceptance or rejection of other people; shame and humiliation are less of a threat for the cog in the wheel than for the lone self. The great sociologist Max Weber talked about the 'unprecedented inner loneliness of the individual self' that the growth of Protestant Christianity caused. Bernard may have freed up the individual self in some ways, but the individual's role in the salvation of his or her soul became even greater after the Lutheran revolution.

This inner loneliness makes feeling in control important for my mind and body. So much of my life is spent trying to engineer the good opinion of others and to avoid negative judgements of *me*. If that 'me' is threatened, my body will spew out more stress hormones and rust up my immune system more than it would for almost any other stress. And in the most extreme situations, such threats can be fatal.

Primo Levi wrote of the Salonica Jews: 'their aversion to gratuitous brutality, their amazing consciousness of the survival of at least a potential of human dignity, made the Greeks the most coherent national nucleus in Lager, and in this respect, the most civilized'.[24] The Salonica Jews, in other words, knew how to save their selves by utilising the strength of the group. Null Achtzehn, on the other hand, had abandoned the struggle to keep his self alive and as a result had lost not only control – but any *wish* for control. After all, with no self, there was nothing to control *for*. The death of Null Achtzehn's self would lead inevitably to the extinction of his body. This awful, extreme example starkly illustrates how fundamental the robustness of the self is for the well-being of the body.

And so we come back to the Oscars. Could it be that the gleaming statuettes offer some protection from threat to the self, and hence a protection from the murderous stress that surfaces when the self is threatened? Before I answer that, let's return to the Second World War – but away from the frozen misery of Auschwitz and instead to the damp fear of London.

The London Blitz was the first mass indiscriminate bombing from the air of a major city in history, with one exception: Britain's Admiral Lord Nelson attacked Copenhagen in Denmark in 1807 with a rocket barrage that destroyed much of that city and killed 2,000 civilians. But the death toll that Hermann Goering's Luftwaffe inflicted on the civilian population of London and other cities in Britain ran to over 40,000. The raids took place at night, in part because the darkness doubled the terror they struck in the hearts of citizens. This terror was part of Hitler's strategy to soften up the British for his planned invasion via the English Channel.

As anyone who suffers from anxiety will know, fear can be conditioned. If you are anxious about public speaking, for instance, that fear is not only triggered by standing on the stage in front of your audience. No, things that are linked to it can become so-called 'conditioned stimuli' for the anxiety: a glimpse of the slide presentation software open on your laptop; seeing the person who chaired your last presentation; or just walking into a lecture hall. These conditioned stimuli acquire the power to trigger your fear: they are major reasons why a quite specific phobia can spread into your life and plague you with anxieties that extend beyond the limited situations of which you are fearful.

And so it was for the people of London. For some, darkness became the trigger for fear, but for most the conditioned stimulus was much more specific – the dreaded wail of the air-raid sirens howling in the night, driving mothers and their drowsy babies down into garden dug-outs or the cold, damp tunnels of the Tube.

The siren was a fear signal – even without the terrifying bombardment that often followed it; its wailing, rising sound sent many Londoners' hearts racing and brought a clammy sweat to their skin. As this happened night after night – whether or not the German bombers came – the prolonged stress took its toll on the bodies and brains of Londoners. Their cortisol-infused blood coursed around their bodies, weakening their immune systems, coating their arteries, swelling their adrenal glands and – particularly among those who felt out of control – shrinking the brain cells in the hippocampal memory centres of their brains.

When mice are exposed to the equivalent of the air-raid warning siren – tones that have become conditioned fear stimuli – they also show signs of fearfulness and even depression and despair.[25] But something quite different happens when they hear a different sound. The exhausted Londoners would stumble out into the daylight to that sound – the low, relieved sigh of the sustained, single-toned 'all clear' siren (listen to http://www.youtube.com/watch?v=erMO3mooLvs for examples of the air-raid warning sound followed by the 'all clear'). That sound signalled one thing: safety – the absence of bombs, the end of death and injury and freedom from terror.

For the mice, the equivalent sound is a tone that is never linked with stress and fear and so predicts nothing except an absence of fear, that is, safety. For many people, coming home after a stressful day of work has that quality – a set of sounds, smells and other stimuli that predict that we won't be stressed. For them, home is a safety signal offering reassurance that they will not be subject to stress. For others, unfortunately, where work intrudes in the home, or where home has its own stresses, returning to the house offers no such safety signals.

The remarkable thing about safety signals is that they do not just predict that stress is off the agenda – they act as antidotes to some of the damaging effects of stress. In the presence of these safety signals, mice shake off fear, depression, despair – and their brains even generate new brain cells in the key memory centres. The safety tones also trigger the release of an important chemical in the brain – Brain-Derived Neurotrophic Factor, or BDNF – a sort of brain fertiliser that helps foster new connections in the brain. Safety signals, then, actually *inhibit* stress and its toxic consequences. And so we return to the gleaming gold of the Oscar statuette and ask: could this be one big safety signal for the fragile self?

The biggest day-to-day stress for us humans is the threat to the self. For most celebrity actors, only as good their last movie, the self is under constant evaluation, repeated threat. The same is true for international scientists, only as good as their last paper, their past achievements having set the bar at heights they have to exceed again and again. Or the salesperson, only as good as the last contract landed. After all, people do not compare the director's new movie, the scientist's new scientific paper or the businessman's latest deal with his average achievement. They compare it with the most easily remembered previous movie/ paper/deal – which is usually the best one.

And that is the proposed solution to the mystery of the Oscars – winning an Oscar may offer a powerful and near-everlasting 'safety signal for self' – a sort of lifelong insurance policy that protects 'me' against the terrible stress of other people's negative evaluations. Winning an Oscar may be one big lifelong 'all clear' air-raid siren – a permanent safety signal that your self is secure. That is perhaps why winning an Oscar makes you live so much longer – by protecting your self, it defends your body.

And that is a very impressive upside of winning. But does the struggle to protect this fragile and elusive self have a downside? Surely to have several billion people on the planet all struggling to win in order to immortalise their individual egos must have costs as well as benefits? That leads to the final question of the book – does winning have a downside? – and to the final puzzle, the riddle of the flying CEOs.

The Riddle of the Flying CEOs

Does winning have a downside?

On 18 November 2008, two months after the 'Black Sunday' collapse of Lehman Brothers and Merrill Lynch, when it looked as if there would be no more cash in the ATMs and a 1929 meltdown was on the cards, three CEOs made their way to Washington to beg for money. Rick Wagoner of GM, Alan Mulally of Ford and Robert Nardelli of Chrysler asked the US government for $25 billion to bail out their near-bankrupt companies. Their corporations had responded to the changing market for automobiles in the US not by planning for new, more fuel-efficient designs, for example, but rather by building big, doomed dinosaurs and selling them cheap.

To the open-mouthed amazement of the press corps waiting for the arriving executives to address the Senate, each one of these three men arrived in Washington on his own corporate jet. GM's luxury $36-million aircraft in which Rick Wagoner arrived, for instance, was only one of a fleet of GM corporate planes at the disposal of executives who had presided over the threatened extinction of their product lines. Even the outrage of a nation and its press could not penetrate whatever bubble these corporations were encased in: ABC News, for instance, reported that: 'GM and Ford say that it is a corporate decision to have their CEOs fly on private jets and that is non-negotiable, even as the companies say they are running out of cash.'[1] Within two weeks, however, the CEOs were driving back to Washington in their best environmentally friendly cars to beg once more for money, and Ford and GM announced that they would be terminating their corporate jet fleets.[2]

How could highly intelligent, meticulously selected business leaders seem so oblivious to the public perception of their behaviour? This is a question relevant to everyone, because we all sometimes do things which we may look back on later and think, 'Did I really do that?' Major lapses of judgement happen to the most intelligent and successful people and they can cost us dear and sabotage our attempts to be winners. But is there a link between success and such lack of judgement? Is there something about winning that distorts judgement? Solving the riddle of the flying CEOs will help answer this question. To do so, let's first take a look at another CEO who also flew – but, in his case, too close to the capitalist sun.

Selling the weather

Fifteen miles south-west of downtown Denver sits a complex of squat, white concrete buildings. In this US Federal Correctional Institution in Lakewood, Colorado, inmate 29296–179 contemplates his release date of 21 February 2028. From time to time perhaps he wonders what he will do that day as he steps out to square his ageing shoulders against an icy wind sweeping off the Rocky Mountain snowfields. At other times, perhaps Jeffrey K. Skilling reflects on his time as the all-powerful CEO of Enron, then the sixteenth-largest corporation in the world.

Enron's Annual Report for the millennium year of 2000 has a slightly dizzying quality to it: just the first line of the accounts alone sends a little shiver through your body – revenues of $100 billion for the year, a staggering increase over the $40 billion for 1999. Imagine the visceral thrill of pleasure that would have run through the bodies of Enron's shareholders at the time.

The traders who bought Enron shares, the market analysts who urged them on, and the shareholders who watched the stock's thrilling rise with glee and gratitude were gratified but unsurprised to see Skilling ranked no lower than number two in *Worth* magazine's annual survey of the fifty best CEOs in 2001 – 'hypersmart and hyperconfident', this respected business publication had gushed about Skilling, according to the *New York Times*.[3]

BusinessWeek was no less enthusiastic in its article about Skilling; on 15 May 2000, it wrote: 'When Enron Corp President Jeffrey K. Skilling takes key customers on an annual trip, it's no sedate golf outing. Instead, Skilling has led such jaunts as a 1,000-mile dirt-bike expedition in Mexico and a seven-day trek through the Australian Outback. No surprise, but Skilling, 46, doesn't limit his thrill-seeking to leisure time. His adventurous spirit has helped revolutionize the way natural gas and electricity are traded in the U.S. As deregulation swept those markets over the past decade, Skilling's once-sleepy pipeline company adapted to become the nation's leading power merchant.'[4]

Skilling did not stop at energy. He also set up systems for trading other 'commodities' such as Internet bandwidth. But perhaps his most notorious achievement in establishing new markets was when he began to trade *weather*. Here is what the 2000 Enron Annual Report said about it: 'Weather has never been better for us. Our weather risk management business is up about five-fold to 1,629 transactions in 2000 from 321 transactions the year

before. As in all of our markets, we bring cross-commodity capa-
bilities to our weather products. For instance, we closed a three-
year precipitation transaction that provides financial compensation linked to natural gas prices if precipitation falls below
a pre-determined minimum. The weather unit worked with
several other Enron groups to transfer Enron's risk, ultimately
transacting with 10 external companies in three markets (natural
gas, weather products and insurance). The bundled end-product
resulted in an effective hedge for the customer.'[5]

Such 'weather derivatives' are essentially bets about what
the weather will be in a given period, and the bets can be
made more complex by linking them to the price of natural
gas or other energy sources which are affected by the weather.
Umbrella makers, for instance, might have placed bets on
Enron's online derivatives trading site that would have paid
off had the seasonal rainfall fallen below a predetermined
amount. More standard derivatives include bets on the future
price of copper, which has at least a real underlying value
in the market; weather has no intrinsic value but in spite of
this, weather derivatives were bought and sold through Enron
Online. Enron Online was essentially an online gambling
set-up on an enormous scale.

Jeffrey K. Skilling was riding high and he knew it. He was on
fire and his legendary arrogance spelled untold riches for Enron,
its shareholders, bond traders – and for him.

Then Skilling suddenly and inexplicably resigned on 14 August
2001, citing personal reasons. On 2 January of that vertiginous
year, the Enron share price had reached $84.06. At close of busi-
ness on 14 August, minutes before Skilling resigned, it stood at
$42.93, falling to a low of $36.87 the next morning when the
news of his departure reached the unsettled markets. On the last
day of 2001, Enron shares were selling for sixty cents.

The catastrophic collapse that Skilling presided over wiped out billions of dollars and the pensions of thousands of loyal employees. In 2001 this seemed so extraordinary, so grotesque a collapse that the press, business analysts, politicians and share-holders sought for explanations in the personalities and/or psychopathologies of the Enron leaders such as CEO Skilling, President Kenneth Lay and Chief Financial Officer Andrew Fastow. How could such a successful business be brought to its knees by making such terrible recruitment mistakes for its most senior positions? Surely the headhunters and selection consult-ants would have to up their game to better select for senior posi-tions in such corporations?

Enron's trading was based on a network of complicated trans-actions, many of which related to deals and events years in the future. As any gambler will tell you, anyone can lose, and indeed, many of Enron's gambles on the future cost of energy were losing money. To conceal this, a rather dubious series of 'partnerships' was created. As it turned out, these were Enron devices for holding debts off the main Enron balance sheet and thus keeping profits dizzyingly high and shareholders ecstati-cally happy. Only when a few shrewd and suspicious journalists began to look behind the delirium of profit did the whole house of cards fall down. How could a group of super-smart winners – the most senior Enron staff – let this happen?

And how, for that matter, did the flying CEOs fail to avoid the obvious PR catastrophe of their corporate flights into Washington? At their stratospheric salary, benefit, pension and share options levels, surely the ability to read and anticipate the public mood was a basic minimum requirement for such a senior executive job? How do we explain this riddle? Strange as it may seem, we should take a look at a condition called 'restless legs syndrome'.

The lady with restless legs

It came to the point where she dreaded going to bed at night. The sensations in her legs – a need to move them – felt as if they were crawling under her skin in a deep, unscratchable 'itch'. 'Kate' – not her real name – had recently turned fifty and had had enough. She was constantly tired from lack of sleep, and also worn down by the alien impulses in her legs. So she went to her doctor, who diagnosed 'restless legs syndrome' and prescribed a medication – pramipexole – which often helps the condition.

Kates's legs did indeed become less jumpy and she felt relieved and rested. But then something very strange happened. Kate didn't gamble and in fact, disapproved of it. She felt that gamblers were unfortunate individuals. But soon after she started taking the pramipexole, she made her way to a nearby casino, where she began to place bets. Her restless legs, though improved, still troubled her, and her physician increased the dose of pramipexole. The legs got better, but her urge to gamble escalated into a compulsion and she started to lose a lot of money.

Two and a half years later, Kate found herself at the Sleep Disorders Clinic in the world-famous Mayo Clinic, where the physicians changed her drug to ropinirole. As they increased the dose, so Kate's gambling compulsion escalated to the point where she lost more than $140,000. Her Mayo Clinic doctors took her off the ropinirole and her desire to gamble was turned off like a light switch.[6]

Pramipexole is also used to treat Parkinson's Disease. Another group of Mayo Clinic doctors[7] were studying the case of 'Jim' – not his real name – who had developed Parkinson's Disease as a relatively young man. At forty-one, Jim had never gambled in his life. His doctors put him on pramipexole and within one month of getting a high dose he became obsessed with gambling on the Internet. He lost $5,000 in a few months. On top of that, he became a compulsive shopper, buying things he neither needed nor really wanted. As soon as the drug was stopped, he switched back to his old self. Why?

Ropinirole and pramipexole increase levels in the brain of the chemical messenger dopamine. They can sometimes help restless legs syndrome for reasons that are not well understood but which may be linked to minor disruption of the brain's dopamine-controlled movement system. These drugs also help raise the low levels of dopamine which are a feature of Parkinson's Disease. But why should they turn some people into compulsive gamblers?

Neuroscience researcher Dr Birgit Abler and her colleagues from the University of Ulm in Germany looked into this question by gathering a group of women like Kate who were taking dopamine agonists for their restless legs. The women were then asked to gamble for real money while in an fMRI scanner, once while they were 'on' the drug and once while 'off' it. While off the dopamine-enhancing drug, their brains – and in particular an area called the ventral striatum where the brain sorts out whether things are rewarding or not – behaved normally. But when on the sort of drug that Kate took, their ventral striatums behaved very strangely.

If you get a letter saying you have won a lottery, this improbable, *unexpected* event will cause a surge in dopamine in your ventral striatum, which will make you feel very good indeed. If you bet on the favourite in a horse race and win, there will be a small surge of dopamine, but nothing to write home about – this is an *expected* reward. If, on the other hand, you find out that you have not won the lottery, then there will be a small drop in dopamine consistent with the mild, expected, but nevertheless disappointing outcome. And if you put a large bet on the favourite, confident that you will win, and unexpectedly the nag falls, you will experience a big and painful drop in dopamine in the ventral striatum.

Dopamine is the juice of reward, which tells us what to learn and do more of and what to unlearn and do less of. In the competition for survival in the evolutionary struggle, those who paid particular attention to unexpected, as opposed to predictable, rewards were better placed to find new sources of food, water, shelter and warmth, and so were more likely to survive to pass on their genes. Equally advantageous was paying attention to unexpected disappointments – the empty water hole or the fruitless tree – as these would act as prompts to explore and avoid such life-threatening disappointments in future.

This is why lottery operators throughout the world are so keen to publicise the enormous rewards of the million-to-one winners: such rare – and therefore unpredicted – rewards cause enormous dopamine surges in the winners. But for the millions of lottery losers, because their loss was *predicted,* it did not result in a painful drop in dopamine. On the contrary, it may be that seeing the dopamine-triggered joy of the lucky winner on television may actually trigger a glimmer of vicarious pleasure in these millions, thus encouraging them to keep buying tickets week after week against all betting odds.

Abler and her colleagues discovered that, when on the drug, the twelve women showed a topsy-turvy response to winning and losing in their ventral striatum. Bizarrely, when the equivalent of the favourite falling in the race happened – i.e., a highly expected reward *didn't* come – they had a rush of dopamine, rather than a drop. And, when the equivalent of the lottery win happened – i.e., a very unexpected reward *did* come – they showed a drop in dopamine signal in the ventral striatum. These women were not problem gamblers, but the dopamine agonist drugs of the kind that Kate took had altered their brain chemistry, so that rather than experiencing a 'down' when their big, highly probable bet didn't come through, they seemed to experience the dopamine equivalent of a 'high'.

Gambling is pleasurable for many people because of the anticipation of winning as well as the occasional win. This feeling of pleasure depends on the brain's dopamine system but in compulsive gamblers the normal response to surprising wins and losses is disrupted, just as it was in Abler's women with restless legs. For most people, the sudden drop in dopamine that would be triggered by a big unexpected loss – say, the favourite horse falling at the last fence – would be experienced as emotionally painful and incline them to learn to avoid such situations in future. For compulsive gamblers, however, because of disruption to their dopamine reward system, they may not experience the same painful drop in dopamine in response to big, unexpected losses, and so do not learn to avoid them.

So, the thrill that you feel when the fruit machine gushes out a clinking cascade of coins is caused by the dopamine surge in the ventral striatum of the brain. But, for Kate and Jim, the drugs they had been given upset the normal functioning of their reward system, and research suggests that this can lead to both an increased craving[8] for the thrill of gambling, as well as a breaking of the normal arithmetic of the pleasure of the win and aching pain of the loss. In the women's brains, an unexpected win produced a mild, dull negative response in the ventral striatum, while failure caused an enlivening surge there. Little wonder that Kate lost $140,000 if the big loss in the casino gave her a dopamine-induced thrill.

But why had restless-leg Germans not become compulsive gamblers as Kate had? The reason for this may lie in a sister part of the brain called the orbito-frontal cortex, which, unlike the striatum, was unaffected by the drug. This part of the brain is important for inhibiting urges and so it is likely that the restless-leg women may have experienced more urges to gamble than before, but that these were quickly dampened down by their healthy and normally functioning inhibitory machinery. We don't know this for sure, but perhaps Kate, Jim and the other minority of people taking these drugs who develop gambling problems have pre-existing vulnerabilities which make it harder for them to quell the dopamine-induced urges that the drugs kindled. Or, alternatively, it could be that they were people to whom gambling was readily available and that other equally vulnerable people not exposed to opportunities for gambling simply never had the chance to encounter the consequences of their vulnerability.

But how do restless legs help us solve the riddle of the flying CEOs? Is there a hint of a solution in the operation of the brain's dopamine system? Yes, there is, but to understand how, we should cast our thoughts back and invoke in our minds a glimmer of that shareholder *thrill* as we read of Enron's dizzying revenue surging to $100 billion for the year 2000, up from a meagre $40 billion for the last year of the tired old nineties. With that thrill lightly primed in our brains and bodies, let us consider some matters . . . ahem . . . sexual.

Ruby the Heart Stealer and the Maharaja of Patiala

Moroccan Karima el-Mahroug – otherwise known to billionaire ex-prime minister of Italy Silvio Berlusconi as 'Ruby the Heart Stealer' – was seventeen when, it is alleged, she attended a 'bunga

bunga' party at Berlusconi's mansion. Italian prosecutors have alleged that then 74-year-old had paid her for sex during what he called his 'bunga bunga' festivities, allegedly involving up to twenty semi-naked women dressed in various costumes.[9]

In announcing her intention to divorce her husband in 2009, following another encounter between Berlusconi and another young woman in Naples, Berlusconi's wife raised the question as to whether her husband was sick. Ruby the Heart Stealer's tale is only one allegation of many involving multiple sexual encounters with an array of different women that surround the septuagenarian, leading to as much condemnation from some parts of Italian society as it does grudging admiration from others.

But the link between sexual potency and political office has never been quite so formalised as in one particular region of north-west India. The Punjab is a place of climatic extremes – icy Himalayan winds searing the alluvial plain in winter and choking heat swelling out of the south in summer. The Maharajas of Patiala ruled the region for hundreds of years, though their line of inherited power was lost when the state of India emerged in 1948.

The Maharajas of Patiala were famous for their jewellery, but in particular for one piece. This was a diamond breastplate that dazzled with the 1,001 blue-white diamonds with which it was encrusted.[10] Until the turn of the seventeenth century, this breastplate was worn by the Maharaja every year on a particular day. On that day, the Maharaja would appear in front of his adoring subjects in his breastplate, buck naked and sporting an erection. As he solemnly paraded around, his delighted subjects would applaud the princely phallus with gusto and enthusiasm. This was a magic swelling endowed with power to ward off evil and protect his grateful subjects,

These are just two extreme examples out of many that illustrate the linkage between money, power and sex. What might

otherwise appear to be a salacious diversion from the puzzle of
the Flying CEOs is actually very relevant to the central question
of this chapter if we look a little more into what happened to Jim,
who was stricken by Parkinson's Disease at a young age. When
he was prescribed the new dopamine-boosting drug, not only
did he start to gamble compulsively – his sex drive also surged
to the point that he sought to make love to his wife several times
a day. And, as with the gambling, when he stopped taking the
drug his sexual behaviour returned to its previous levels.

But the flying CEOs were not exposed to dopamine-raising
drugs, nor were their sex lives abnormal. So how does this help
solve the riddle of the flying CEOs? Read on.

You don't know it, but you may have a particular variation of a
gene which affects the amount of dopamine circulating in the
synapses of the reward parts of your brain. The gene I have in
mind is called the 10 repeat allele of the DAT1 gene. You will
have inherited none, one or two copies of it. This gene affects
how much dopamine is available in the striatum, the brain
region where these all-important reward centres are located. We
have found in my laboratory that healthy children who had two
copies of this gene were less likely to notice brief flashes on the
left side of a computer screen than on the right: their attention,
in other words, was deflected slightly to the right. They were also
more prone to making impulsive and absent-minded errors on
a concentration test.[11] Certain alleles of this gene also increase
the likelihood of a diagnosis of attention deficit hyperactivity
disorder and are described as 'risk alleles'.

What, you may ask, has this finding got to do with Silvio
Berlusconi and the Maharaja of Patiala? A quick visit to a team
at the University of North Carolina helps explain: Guang Guo
and colleagues studied the effects of the DAT1 gene in 2,500

adolescents whom they studied and interviewed over a period of approximately seven years into early adulthood. Guo's team were interested in the question of sexually transmitted diseases in this age group, and so wanted to understand why some adolescents had more sexual partners than others.

Because of the DAT1's role in dopamine and impulsive behaviour, they counted the number of sexual partners of adolescents with two copies of the gene – the sort whose attention was biased to the right and who made impulsive errors on my concentration tests – and compared this with the number of sexual partners of those who had only one or no copies of the DAT1 risk allele.

The results were remarkable: in the eighteen- to twenty-three-year-old men, those with no copies of the high-risk DAT1 allele reported that they had had sexual intercourse with an average of two different people since they were first interviewed several years earlier. When it came to the young men who had two copies of the high-risk allele, they reported an average of over five different sexual partners in the same period. But this was only true for men – women's number of sexual partners was unrelated to their DAT1 profile.

Another gene, DRD4, also influences dopamine levels in the brain. Working in my and my colleague Michael Gill's laboratories, Mark Bellgrove and others discovered that attention deficit disordered children with two copies of a particular allele of the DRD4 gene were also more absent-minded and impulsive in concentration tests than similar children who did not have the two copies.[12] And, elsewhere, a group of cash-hungry Harvard students showed that this particular gene also affected their willingness to take real financial risks.

Anna Dreber and her colleagues at Harvard University asked students who did or did not have at least one copy of this dopamine gene to play a financial investment game which had a real pay-off. Each student was given a notional balance of $250 and was asked to select an 'investment' – really a bet – of between zero and $250 to place on the flip of a coin. If he (they were all male) lost, he lost the stake. If he won, then he won back two and a half times his stake.

A cautious, risk-averse person could guarantee keeping $250 dollars by just betting zero. A risk-hungry gambler, on the other hand, would readily bet large amounts of money and be equally likely to end up with zero as with the maximum, $625. Even Harvard, however, could not afford to pay real cash to the players, but what Dreber did was to tell the students that at the end of the study they would draw a lot and in this way one of them *would* receive the actual amount of money he had won – so the bets did have real financial meaning to the players.

It's not difficult to guess what Dreber found: the students who had the DRD4 pattern that seemed to make the children impulsive and absent-minded in my laboratory risked significantly more money in the Harvard experiment than did those without that gene. She and her colleagues went on to study real-life risk-taking during the 2008 North American Bridge Championship in Boston, Massachusetts, and found that men with one or two copies of the DRD4 allele were significantly more inclined to take risks in their bids than men who did not.[13]

In Chapter 2 we saw how London traders made more profit on days when their testosterone was high: the common linkage here is dopamine, the brain chemical associated with thrill, whether it be the thrill of gambling and risk, or the thrill of sex. Testosterone racks up dopamine levels, which then boost the appetite for thrill.

Dopamine, then, is a common currency of desire, whether it be for gambling or sex. And it is the high value and exchangeability of this currency that explains why gambling and sex are over-whelmingly dominant in the Internet economy.

Jeffrey Skilling's thrilling hikes in Enron profits were part of the vast casino that was Enron. Enron was known as the 'millionaire factory' where young, clever, ambitious recruits were encouraged to develop new derivatives and new markets in which to trade them – even the weather. In Skilling's brain, his dopamine system would have been racked up by this non-stop, high-stakes gambling – just as it was for many Wall Street traders of 2007 before their gigantic financial bubble collapsed.

Financial trading can be like gambling on a vast scale. Bets are made on such things as the future prices of real commodities as well as on abstract things like whether share prices will rise or fall, whether nations will default on their sovereign debt and so on. Enron took this betting into new realms through its online trading platforms, where enormous bets could be made in matters of seconds, and through the range of things that could be gambled on – the weather being the most unusual example.

And the thrill of the Enron gambling was a generic one that shares a brain pathway with the sexual pleasure that Ruby the Heart Stealer likely triggered in Silvio Berlusconi. But can such activities, in excess and with constant repetition, become addictive? Are the visceral rewards of earthly pleasures – winning among them – routed through a central area in the brain, a reward exchange that deals in these goodies? And can overloading of this system lead to addiction to these pleasures?

A large chunk of the world's economy revolves around sex and gambling. But there is a third commodity around which another gigantic global economy circulates – drugs. Could gambling and sex be like addictive drugs that drive people to extremes of rationality-defying behaviour?

Indeed they can be. My colleague Hugh Garavan has shown that cocaine thrills in very similar ways to the entirely natural reward – sex – and indeed like other rewards such as the money used in gambling.[14] Drugs like cocaine and heroin hijack a reward system that we evolved to help us learn to seek out pleasant and helpful experiences and avoid painful ones. But their sheer undiluted infusion into the ventral striatum and linked brain areas can, like high-dose gambling or sex, disrupt the natural functioning of the reward system so that the behaviour becomes compulsive and self-destructive.[15] When the reward system is hijacked in this way, it creates a vicious cycle of tolerance, in which ever-higher levels are needed to achieve the same 'high'.

Kristin Davis pleaded guilty to running New York's biggest and most pricey upmarket prostitution agency in 2008 and served four months in New York's Rikers Island penitentiary. Her escort service included among its customers a large number of Wall Street investment bankers and CEOs, who, according to her testimony, would often bill her $2,000-per-hour services to their corporate credit cards. While that assertion is not scientifically verified observation, the high-risk gambling of Wall Street may have, in some genetically vulnerable male financial traders in particular, screwed up their dopamine systems sufficiently to leave them in a state of restless, gnawing craving for the next high-voltage dopamine fix, and for some that could be supplied interchangeably by gambling, sex – or cocaine.

The enormous salaries and bonuses of the flying CEOs may not have had the same thrilling quality of gambling that made the air of Houston, Texas, crackle with Enron energy, and there is no evidence of sexual compulsion on their part, nor of any use of illegal drugs. But there is one other commodity that drives the reward system with an insistent vigour and which the flying CEOs had in abundance – *power*.

As we saw in Chapter 3, power causes testosterone surges, which in turn trigger dopamine release. When the former US Secretary of State and bon viveur Henry Kissinger commented that power is the greatest aphrodisiac, he may have been speaking from experience, and from a neuroscience perspective he was spot on. And anything – money, sex, power or cocaine – that strongly and repeatedly triggers surges of dopamine in the brain's reward system runs the risk of unleashing the unquenchable cravings of the addict.

Silvio Berlusconi very likely has a high personal need for power, and Oliver Schultheiss and his colleagues at the University of Michigan have shown that men and women with a high need for power have sex much more often than those with lower levels.[16] And both men and women with higher levels of power are more likely to be unfaithful in their relationships.[17] Even if Berlusconi does not have the dopamine genes which leave him lustful for sex and high-stakes risk, the huge power he holds in Italy through his control of most of the television channels, his enormous wealth and high political office would in any case have primed his sexual appetites through their combined effects on his brain's dopamine system.

On its own, power is not automatically sexually arousing for many men. But for those with tolerant attitudes to sexual harassment – for instance, those who say that they would consider asking sexual favours of a woman in exchange for giving her a lucrative contract – thoughts of power turn them on sexually. When small amounts of power are unconsciously 'primed' in their minds by getting them to complete fragmented words which have (unknown to the men) power connotations, they find a female stranger in the same room

to be more attractive than if they are subliminally exposed
to neutral words. This is true even though the power-words
have nothing obviously to do with sex.[18] Men who do not
have attitudes favourable to sexual harassment, on the other
hand, don't show any increase in the rated attractiveness of
the woman stranger when they are similarly unconsciously
primed with thoughts of power.

When the habitual cocaine user sees a rolled-up banknote,
notices a picture of white powder or finds himself in a party
atmosphere, his racked-up, primed-for-action reward system
will spurt out a much bigger surge of anticipatory dopamine
than a novice user's would; and that surge of dopamine he
experiences as craving. But this is not specific to the drug – the
compulsive gambler and the sex addict, whose reward systems
are similarly geared up, can also experience such a dopamine-
mediated craving, which, in a disrupted system, can never fully
be satisfied.

And this may be part of the reason why, in early 2011,
President Hosni Mubarak of Egypt, even at the age of eighty-
two, found it so hard to stand down. It may also explain why,
only a few weeks later, Colonel Gaddafi of Libya preferred to
strafe his unarmed and peacefully protesting citizens from helicopter gunships than relinquish any of his power.

Power can corrupt, and one reason that it may do so is that it
is a very powerful drug which can, in high and repeated doses,
become addictive. The addictive qualities of power, and its
distorting effects on the human mind, have caused the deaths
of hundreds of millions of people in the past century alone,
through other power-addicted, dopamine-disregulated dictators like Stalin, Mao, Kim Il Sung, Hitler, Mugabe, Pol Pot and
many others.

And it also happens in a much less pernicious form to some senior executives of major corporations, leading to a whole series of personality changes as exemplified by Jeffrey Skilling. While at Enron, Skilling displayed a legendary arrogance which may have played a part in the company's collapse. His contempt for his underlings was also extreme. A former executive recalled an incident when Skilling roared past a line of staff in their automobiles waiting to enter the Enron car park, raising his middle finger in response to their frustrated honks of protest. Here was a man who in his mid-forties was known for his intense, thrill-seeking adventures in Mexico and Australia, but who as a student was described by someone who knew him as 'middle of the road, nothing outstanding, nothing controversial, a nice guy'.[19]

Did this sort of change in attitude explain the flying CEOs as well? Did their dopamine-reward systems, primed by power and bonuses, blind them to the viewpoint of others, permitting their insensitive behaviour? Maybe, but this explanation does not entirely satisfy. Arrogance is common among successful leaders. The flying CEOs did not, to our knowledge, display the type of arrogance that Skilling displayed, and their corporations were not guilty of the sorts of practices that Enron engaged in. But many highly paid, powerful executives seem to be at risk of bizarre behaviour with Sir Fred Goodwin's alleged preoccupation with pink wafers just as his company, the Royal Bank of Scotland, was about to implode being a particularly good example.

Most senior executives are not, however, compulsive gamblers. Is there anything else that could account for their behaviour? Let's turn to golf for a possible answer.

An expensive putt

The ball was only three feet from the hole and Tiger Woods hunched over it, taking a few moments to visualise it sinking into the hole, a habit of mental preparation he learned from his late father. It was the sixteenth hole of the play-off against Irishman Padraig Harrington, and Woods was comfortably in the lead – until he missed.

Maybe it was the weather – four degrees Celsius under a chilly Japanese sky for the 2006 Dunlop Phoenix Tournament. Or perhaps it was the fact that the upstart Irishman had just holed a magnificent birdie. But there is one other possible explanation for the stroke that, given what we now know about winning and the brain, probably provides a better explanation. That three-foot putt was worth forty million Japanese Yen – $482,000[20] – and more importantly to a wealthy champion like Woods, it was worth an awful lot more in status, pride and reputation.

It was the crucial stroke of the play-off – Woods went on to fluff another putt on the seventeenth hole, leaving Harrington to tap in an easy shot in the last hole. That sixteenth-hole 'choke' had begun the rot that eliminated the lead he had built up in three early birdies. What was happening in Woods's mind to make him choke like that?

Christopher Frith and his colleagues from University College London decided to see whether such 'choking' was purely something that only pampered celebrity sports personalities succumbed to.[21] They scanned the brains of a group of volunteer students who had to try to capture a 'prey' in a maze in a computer game. Frith's group compared the effect of big versus small rewards on their performance, but rather than offer them a few million dollars' bonus and a private jet in return for winning, they instead tempted the impoverished student players on some trials with a low (roughly $1) and on others a high (roughly $10) reward for catching the prey.

Now if you happen to hold shares in a corporation with multi-million-dollar bonus schemes for its executives, you might prefer to skip to the next page. Remarkably, the $10 reward seems to have made the players 'choke' in much the same way that the $500,000 prize and anticipated glory made Tiger Woods miss that thirty-six-inch putt. When tantalised by a $10 reward for winning, the players succeeded only 63 per cent of the time, compared with 74 per cent when the reward was a modest $1. What has this got to do with dopamine, though?

The answer is this – the worse the player did, the more activity Frith and his colleagues saw in the dopamine-rich reward region of the ventral midbrain. What's more, they found that the players who said that they wanted the money most showed the biggest midbrain activity. In other words, not only did high rewards turn winning into losing – the more you wanted to win, the more likely you were to lose – but the most likely culprit was a surfeit of dopamine-fuelled motivation. They *wanted* it too much and that excess of desire interfered with the ability to do the job well and win. After Padraig Harrington's startlingly good birdie on that sixteenth hole, and with an impressive record of tournament wins to live up to, Woods *wanted* to hole that ball very badly indeed, probably less for the financial stake than for the sake of pride and status.

It is hard to ignore Frith's findings when you consider that one of the flying CEOs – Alan Mulally of Ford – received no less than $28 *million* for four months' work in 2007, as he took over a corporation which posted a *loss* of $12.7 *billion* in 2006.[22] But it is not just money that thrills – in fact, it may be the status that thrills equally. As I showed you in the previous chapter, Oscar winners live longer because of the remarkably protective effects of this status on their lives and sense of self. Could part of money's effects on the brain be via this most crucial of human needs – that for the approval of others?

Indeed it is. Keise Izuma and colleagues from the National Institute for Physiological Sciences in Japan[23] showed that money and status switch on much the same midbrain dopamine systems – the recognition and approval of others gives a surge of pleasure that is similar to that of the winning bet or the teasing sexual caress. Only in very big doses, however, does it produce the tidal surge of dopamine that a snort of cocaine produces.

A certain amount of dopamine, then, invigorates you, motivates you and gives you that glow of well-being that follows reward and recognition. It also sharpens you mentally, and puts a glint in your goal-achieving eye. Above all, it gives you an appetite for *risk*. That may be the main reason why boards pay their CEOs such eye-watering sums of money. In certain respects, it *works*, and it works the way the prospect of sex with a desirable partner works, by racking up the dopamine activity in your reward system and making you do things either that you never thought you could, or that you could not be bothered doing before.

But how does this square with Tiger Woods 'choking' on the sixteenth hole, or Frith's volunteers failing to catch the prey in the computer game? To answer that, we must take a detour into the forest to meet three bears – and a new friend of theirs.

The Goldilocks principle

Goldilocks exasperated the three bears in the fairy tale by wanting her porridge not too hot and not too cold, and her bed not too soft and not too hard. It so happens that this handed-down fairy tale of Goldilocks and the Three Bears doesn't just apply to motivation as we saw in Chapter 1, it also captures a pretty critical feature of how the brain works. Dopamine is a chemical messenger which needs to be in the 'just right' Goldilocks zone to have the best effect on your performance. Too much dopamine disrupts the intricate co-ordination and organisation of connected parts of the brain, while too little leads to poor co-ordination of partner areas of the brain owing to insufficient regulation by dopamine. Parkinson's Disease, for instance, is an example of a brain disorder where the problem is too little dopamine, while schizophrenia, to take another example, is linked to excess dopamine in certain parts of the brain.

Rewards – whether they be money, status, acclaim or sex – can be so big or so often repeated that they take your brain out of the Goldilocks zone, just as the super-reward of drugs like cocaine does. When that happens, the system malfunctions, just as it did with Jim and the restless-legs women whose dopamine was racked up too much by the drugs they were treated with.

Lack of rewards – as manifested in poverty, low status or social rejection – can have the opposite effect: the brain's dopamine sinks below the Goldilocks zone, resulting in listlessness, lack of motivation, anxiousness and over-concern with risk.

We know that dopamine levels surge in proportion to the money, status and power the person possesses. Could it be then, that the flying CEOs were pushed out of the Goldilocks zone because they were over-rewarded? Could this explain their behaviour?

Possibly. But again, there are many excellent CEOs who are similarly rewarded but who do not show the sorts of behaviour that the flying CEOs did. There have to be other ingredients in this particular stew – and one smell from the pot that is particularly strong is that of money.

*   *   *

Try this: see how quickly you can make a four-word meaningful phrase or sentence out of these five words: *cold it desk outside is*. Now try this one: *paper dropped Sally laptop the*. And this one: *long window grass the is*. Now, having solved these word puzzles, imagine that someone asks you at this moment for a donation for a third-world charity. How much will you donate? Make a mental note of this.

Now unscramble these words, again making four-word phrases that make sense: *high a salary desk paying*. Next: *the won he thief lottery*. Finally: *quick got drive rich he*. Now someone else comes up and asks you to donate to an equally worthy charity. Imagining that you have not just donated recently, how much will you give? Is it the same amount as the first time, more – or less?

You might have noticed a difference between the two sets of words: the last three included money-related items, while the first three did not. Kathleen Vohs of the University of Minnesota and her colleagues asked volunteers to solve a large number of puzzles like this, with some of them exposed to money-linked words, and others not. Because they were focused on what they thought was a speed-of-problem-solving task, the students in the money group didn't know that they had been exposed to these money words, but their unconscious mind, on the other hand, *had* 'noticed'.

All the students had been given $2 in quarters at the beginning of the experiment, a part-payment for participating. After they finished the word problems, another student came up to them and asked them to donate to a welfare charity. Would you predict a difference between the two groups? Vohs and her colleagues did, and their predictions were vindicated.

The students in whose minds the concept of money was 'primed' donated significantly *less* money than those who had not. And Vohs went on to make a number of other remarkable observations. Students with money-primed brains were less helpful to a passing student who spilled pencils on the floor beside them: the money-primed group picked up significantly fewer pencils! The money group were also much less helpful to fellow students who feigned confusion about what it was they were supposed to do in an experimental task.

What else did unconscious thoughts of money do? It made people place their chair further away from others, and made them prefer to work alone rather than with others. When given the choice between an individual leisure activity – say, having four individual, personal cooking lessons versus a home-catered meal for four, students who had been primed with thoughts of money opted for the lone activity over the one involving other people.

Why should thoughts of money have such profound effects on people? Vohs and her colleagues argue that money boosts one's sense of self-sufficiency – i.e., feeling of personal control over events and life. This self-sufficiency, they argue, makes people focus on personal goals. Because of this focus on individual goals, they prefer to separate themselves from others – and hence also behave less altruistically and more selfishly. Not having money, on the other hand, can make people feel out of control over events and life – but perhaps also less selfish.

It may seem strange, but money is also linked to thoughts of death: but maybe that is not so strange, given that death is the ultimate loss of control. Money, on the other hand, is the supreme endower of control. Tim Kasser and Kennon Sheldon of Knox College asked volunteers to write short essays about death and found that, compared with those writing essays about a neutral subject, the volunteers had much higher financial expectations for themselves fifteen years hence, including what they would be spending on pleasurable items and activities.[24] They then asked the volunteers to play a forest-management game and found that those who had been exposed to thoughts of death became more greedy and consumed more resources than the control participants.

As you have seen, sex, power, money and cocaine all use the common currency of dopamine and each can rack up the need for the other. The prostitution and cocaine use of highly paid Wall Street traders reported in the 2010 movie *Inside Job* are, like the Wall Street hedges and derivatives, highly liquid commodities and can be transferred easily across domains. Dopamine is like gold – a universally convertible currency.

The flying CEOs probably thought about money a lot. Banks and financial companies use bonuses to incentivise their managers – and they have measurable effects on the brain. But it is not just money which can have these neurological effects: Susanne Erk and her colleagues of the University of Ulm in Germany showed men photographs of sports cars versus smaller, lower-status cars.[25] They found that the higher-status sports vehicles ramped up the ventral striatum of men's brains while they were in the fMRI scanner.

Just looking at a picture of a sports car triggered the reward centres to thrill a certain kind of viewer in the same way that being given a wad of money does. Imagine then, the knee-weakening thrill of pleasure running through Rick, Alan and Robert's brains the first time they saw their private jets on the tarmac waiting to spirit them off to the destination of their choice.

There is only so much dopamine that the human reward system can take. Overload it, and you are likely get the sort of problem that Jim and the restless-legs women did. But the flying CEOs were not compulsive gamblers, and though their brains were almost certainly chronically primed by thoughts of money and dopamine-triggering high-status accoutrements such as private jets, is there something additional that can explain their error of judgement on the day of the flight into Washington?

Who takes the last cookie?

Imagine for a moment that you volunteer for a research project in your local university. The researcher randomly assigns you to a group with two other people of the same gender. You're asked to spend half an hour discussing a number of contentious social issues, your job being to come up with some policy recommendations for tackling them. But here's the catch: one of you strangers is randomly chosen to be in charge – and to judge the performance of the people in the group: this 'boss' assigns grades reflecting the quality of your and others' contributions to the discussion.

Take a moment to imagine yourself in this situation and you will see that this is not a trivial situation – being judged by a stranger about your intellectual contribution is a pretty daunting experience for anyone. That judge has power even if it is only for half an hour. It is a power over your most precious commodity – self-esteem.

At the end of the discussion, the researcher arrives with five cookies on a plate and sets it in the centre of the table. Five cookies, three people – what happens? With only a few exceptions, each of the three participants will take a cookie – leaving just two on the plate – not enough to go round a second time. The volunteers are, of course, being filmed. So who takes a second cookie? In the majority of cases, the randomly selected 'boss', of course. And he or she also shows some interesting changes in behaviour.

Dacher Keltner and colleagues of Stanford University, who carried out this experiment, showed that he or she is much more likely to eat messily – to be socially disinhibited, in other words.[26] The boss tends to munch with an open mouth, leaving crumbs on his or her face and scatter cookie debris on the table. These behaviours, it seems, are not enduring features of a bad upbringing or sloppy personality: if the same person had been selected as one of the other group members, he or she would have eaten demurely and not carelessly.

We saw in Chapter 3 how arousing feelings of power also make people poorer at decoding other people's emotional expressions. The cookie study shows that power also makes people care less about what others think, making them selfish and lacking empathy. Even the tiniest taste of temporary power can make us more egocentric and less inclined to consider other perspectives.

The flying CEOs showed a similar empathy deficit when they flew into Washington: the brains of these immensely powerful men had been shaped by power so that it was difficult for them to see their actions as others saw them.

One consequence of lack of empathy and egocentricity is that it inclines us to see people as a means to our ends – more as *instruments* of our own goals. Professor Deborah Gruenfeld and colleagues at Stanford University have found evidence for precisely this: if we arouse power feelings in otherwise ordinary people, they begin to see others as objects.

When students' brains were primed into a power mode by reliving a situation from their past where they had power over someone, they also were inclined to see others in terms of how useful they were to them. They were, for instance, more likely to report that they contacted people when they needed something from them and they were less likely to report that they really liked a colleague independently of how useful that person was to them.[27]

If brief memories of low-grade power in artificial experiments can make people more egocentric and socially uninhibited and incline them to see other people as objects, what effects does long-term, large-scale power over thousands of people have on the human mind? Gruenfeld had a unique opportunity to answer this question at a gathering of high-level business executives who had long experience of wielding power. True to her predictions, Gruenfeld showed that power-wielding senior business executives were more likely than business students to view people – whether underlings or peers – in terms of their usefulness to them rather than in terms of their non-utilitarian personal qualities.

On 27 September 2002, in a small town near Frankfurt, Germany, eleven-year-old Jakob von Metzler, son of the head of a wealthy banking dynasty, climbed down from the school bus and made his way home. That night his anguished family received a ransom demand, which they paid, but Jakob was not released. Four days later a twenty-seven-year-old law student named Magnus Gäfgen was arrested and confessed to the kidnapping, but even after several hours of questioning, refused to disclose where Jakob was being held.

The deputy police chief of Frankfurt, Wolfgang Daschner, fearing that the boy might die a slow death in a forgotten shed, ordered his subordinates to get Jakob's location from Gäfgen by threatening him that a specialist interrogator was being helicoptered in from Frankfurt to inflict pain on him of the sort he had never experienced before. It took only a few minutes for Gäfgen to direct them to a lake near Frankfurt, where they found Jakob, wrapped in plastic and already dead.[28]

A debate blew up in Germany about the morality of threatening torture, even in such an urgent case. The two contrasting perspectives were of a *rule*-based approach – it is in principle wrong to threaten or use torture – versus an *outcome*-based approach – in this case it is not wrong to do this because it has the chance of saving Jakob's life.

This true story was one of a number that Joris Lammers of Tilburg University and colleagues used to probe the effects of power on people's moral thinking.[29] They asked volunteers to make judgements about the correct decision to take in a number of moral dilemmas. In another example, the girlfriend of a boy who has just been diagnosed with terminal cancer overhears the doctor's diagnosis before the boy does. She begs the doctor not to tell her boyfriend until after they return from a long-planned and very special trip to Africa, which he has always dreamt about visiting. Given he has only six months to live, why not let him enjoy this particular journey unburdened by the knowledge of his fate? The doctor's ethical rules mean that he should tell the boy, but an outcome-based decision – in other words the end justifying the means – would mean he should not tell.

Lammers found that power – whether unconsciously primed in the mind or actually given over other people in an experimental situation – made volunteers much more likely to advocate rule-based decisions, and less likely to advocate outcome-based decisions: minds primed with power were more likely to say that threatening Magnus Gäfgen was wrong and that the doctor should tell the boy about his terminal diagnosis. Minds primed with powerlessness were much more likely to say that threatening torture was justified and that the doctor should let the boyfriend go on holiday without knowing his diagnosis.

Power, then, makes people more moral, or at the very least rule-following – or does it? Were the Enron executives, for instance, ennobled by the vast power they held? Surely this is at odds with the notion that power tends to corrupt? The ingenious Lammers had an answer for that.

Here is another moral scenario which Lammers presented to his volunteers: 'Suppose someone is looking for a new apartment after his landlord has terminated the tenancy. However, the only affordable option is public housing, for which there is a three-year waiting list. There is however a trick that allows him to bypass the waiting list and immediately obtain a house.'

Was using this trick acceptable? Rate this between 1 (definitely not) and 9 (definitely yes).

What happened? In Lammers's volunteers, exactly the same as before – those randomly assigned to a power frame of mind were much more likely to rate it less acceptable than those with minds unprimed by power. But then came the twist. Lammers gave this story to only half the volunteers. The other half read this one: 'Suppose you are looking for a new apartment after your landlord has terminated the tenancy. However, the only affordable option is public housing, for which there is a three-year waiting list. There is however a trick that allows you to bypass the waiting list and immediately obtain a house.'

The first story was one written in the third person about *someone else*, while the second was written about *you*. As soon as the moral judgement became about the readers the effects of power on their minds reversed. Power now made people *less* likely to choose the rule-based judgement, and *more* likely to choose the ends-justifies-means, outcome-based judgement.

This helps explain Skilling's behaviour: he probably presided over highly rule-based guidelines about how employees should behave. Power would likely have made him an assiduous and highly moral implementer of these rules. But that very same power may have inclined him to weaken the rules when applied to himself and instead be more likely to invoke an outcome-based approach to judging his own actions.

Power had blinded Skilling to making the sort of judgements of his own behaviour that others were to make once they knew what was going on. When self-interest comes to the fore, power primes selfishness and a mindset of special-case exceptionalism. Large personal gains in the form of bonuses or personal shares in trading profits magnify this self-interest and hence probably weaken the application of moral standards to oneself.

On 12 January 2010, the *New York Times* published an email that had been sent by Thomas Mazarakis, Head of Fundamental Strategies at the investment bank Goldman Sachs. In the email he said: 'We may trade, and may have existing positions, based on trading ideas before we have discussed those trading ideas with you.'[30] This email confirmed what many had suspected, namely that Goldman Sachs had considerable difficulty in managing the conflicts of interest in balancing the information and advice it gave to its own trading groups, versus that given to its external clients. As an example, Goldman had been selling huge tranches of doomed and toxic mortgages known as collateralised debt obligations while at the same time selling them short – in other words, betting against these very same financial lemons.

Now that is a pretty lucrative position, and may explain why Goldman Sachs came out of the 2008 meltdown in a relatively rosy financial position. After all, hadn't they won both ways, taking in billions for toxic mortgages with one hand and then taking in further billions when the bets they had laid that the mortgages would fail came home?

The conduct of Goldman Sachs makes sense in the light of Lammers's experiments. The enormous power wielded by the bankers and traders may have been funnelled through dizzying amounts of financial self-interest into an outcome-based, rather than a rule-based frame of mind. Power-triggered exceptionalism shielded them, perhaps, from any twinges of conscience about the remarkable darkness of their actions.

As far as we know, the flying CEOs behaved entirely legally and morally but could their vast bonuses, power and privilege have triggered some form of exceptionalism in their minds, making it hard for them to appreciate how each flying into Washington in a separate jet would look to the average person? Yes and no, but there is also another factor.

As CEO of Enron, Jeffrey Skilling reputedly did not care what people's names were and believed in ruthless culling – often on an arbitrary basis – of staff. He brought to Enron the infamous 'rank and yank' system whereby every employee was rated on the intranet by supervisors, colleagues – and indeed by any other employees who cared to log in. In the wake of each six-monthly rank and yank, and irrespective of the actual scores, those in the bottom 15 per cent of ratings were essentially kicked out: they were given a couple of months to find a new job in the organisation, but given that their files were stamped with a big red bottom 15 per cent fail number, most exited the company.

Skilling's management systems were a great source of new patients for local mental health professionals: this, and the treating-others-as-objects disinhibition he displayed as he gave the middle finger to his underlings and forced his way to the head of the line, show that his empathy was pretty blunted. Given his reportedly modest personality while at college, the likely culprits in this are the effects of unfettered power on the brain.

But this is not the only explanation for how Skilling and the flying CEOs behaved, for power has another very important consequence.

The cover of *Time* magazine for 6 April 1987 shows a full-page photograph of multi-millionaire televangelist Jimmy Swaggart, microphone in one hand, index finger of the other raised in admonishment, and his face concentrated into an expression of condemnation.[31] Inset is a photograph of Jim Bakker, competitor televangelist, and his wife. The caption says: 'Unholy Row: TV Preacher Jimmy Swaggart and the Besieged Bakkers.'

Bakker had confessed to an afternoon of 'sin' some years previously with one comely twenty-one-year-old named Jessica Hahn. Jimmy Swaggart's moral condemnation was strident and unforgiving: he called Bakker 'a cancer that needs to be excised from the body of Christ!'. He was equally censorious of another competitor preacher, Marvin Gorman, who like Swaggart had his base in New Orleans, alleging that Gorman had committed adultery, an allegation for which he later had to pay Gorman substantial damages in a libel suit.

Within a year, Jimmy Swaggart had resigned from his Pentecostal Church organisation after pictures were released of him with a prostitute at a New Orleans hotel. His famous sobbing confession to unspecified wrongdoing before the details came out has become an Internet video classic. Having been accepted by his forgiving congregation, more than three years later, on 14 October 1991, he announced that he would step down from his worldwide ministry, following accusations that he had picked up a California prostitute, Rosemary Garcia, in his car. Swaggart's hypocrisy was breathtaking. So was his power over millions of people through his media and church empire, and these two things – power and hypocrisy – may be more closely linked than is at first sight apparent.

In another study, Joris Lammers and his colleagues looked at what effects power had on hypocritical behaviour. First they boosted a sense of power in the volunteers' minds by asking half of them to describe a situation in the past where they had had power, and the other half a situation where they had been under someone else's power.[32] Participants then had to rate how acceptable/unacceptable it was for people to exaggerate their travel expenses.

Lammers predicted that high power makes people feel entitled and hence more comfortable with making judgements about other people's behaviour: true to the prediction, the randomly selected volunteers who had power primed in their minds rated exaggerating travel expenses as significantly more unacceptable than those who had been primed with low power memories.

That was their *judgement* – like Jimmy Swaggart's of Jim Bakker's infidelity. But what about what they actually did? Lammers told the volunteers that as payment for taking part in the study, they could enter a lottery, and they could roll two dice to determine how many lottery tickets they would get, and hence increase or decrease their chance of winning.

The dice were rolled in a cubicle in private and were supposed to be thrown only once. What happened? The people who had been primed with high power memories cheated significantly more than did the low power volunteers. Like Jimmy Swaggart, they were more morally disapproving of what others did, but much more lax with themselves when it came to their own personal moral behaviour. Power, in other words, created hypocrisy.

Lammers and his colleagues went on to manipulate power in different ways – by making someone 'boss' in a group exercise, as in the cookie experiment described earlier. Then they asked students who had been made either powerful or powerless by this manipulation to make moral judgements about the acceptability of three real-life situations – not declaring extra income for tax, keeping an abandoned stolen bicycle and breaking traffic laws to get to an important appointment.

The students then rated how acceptable it was for *them* if they found that they had done any of these things. Sure enough, the high power people were significantly more forgiving of themselves than of others, compared with the low power ones.

Swaggart's behaviour was not unusual, it seems. Hypocrisy is a feature of the rhetoric of many politicians – and by extension of anyone with high levels of power – and it is likely that this power-induced hypocrisy may have played a part in the antics of Skilling and others at Enron. Perhaps hypocrisy is an inevitable adjunct to power – a natural neural correlate of having control over others. If you are in charge, maybe it just seems right that the rule which you apply to others should not apply to you. A sense of exceptionalism and entitlement may even be seen as desirable by some boards of corporations – suggesting the possibility of buccaneering entrepreneurialism and capacity for profit-generating risk.

All CEOs of successful corporations are vulnerable to hypocrisy because of the power they hold, yet most do not go the way of Enron. Only some powerful people become hooked on the dopamine that power, money and institutional gambling trigger, and a proportion become addicted and hence distorted in their judgements as a result. But in any decent-sized organisation there will surely always be some people who are *not* so vulnerable to this corruption of their mental processes. And if that is the case, then these pathologies of the individual executive surely cannot explain the financial disaster of 2007–8 or Enron.

If you get paid for doing a job, the brain's reward system, underpinned by dopamine, will give you a warm glimmer of reward and make it more likely that you will drag yourself out of bed on a cold, wet morning to do that job again, keeping the wolf from the door. It was for this purpose of survival that the dopamine brain reward system evolved.

But suppose that you and your friend do the same job together, and he or she gets paid more than you. Does your brain's reward system take this into account? It does, according to research by Klaus Fliessbach and colleagues from the University of Bonn in Germany.[33] Pairs of volunteers lay in adjacent fMRI scanners while together they played a simple game making quick decisions about the number of dots on a screen – and, importantly, they were paid for correct answers.

It shouldn't be surprising to hear that winning showed up as an increased level of activation in the ventral striatum. But what happened if on some rounds your partner got paid more than you for the same correct answer? After all, you were still getting a reward, so shouldn't the ventral striatum have gratefully released its dopamine? It still does, but much less than it would otherwise, because in comparison with your partner, you won less.

It makes sense – nothing discontents us more than to know that someone else doing a similar job is being paid more than we are. But this study was the first demonstration of what happens in the brain for this type of mental tally. Humans are nothing if not social and what other people are being rewarded or punished for matters hugely to us.

Judging whether we are getting properly rewarded or not can only really be done by comparing ourselves with other people: the courts are littered with cases taken by aggrieved bankers claiming unfair treatment because their enormous bonuses were significantly less than the even more enormous bonus of the bankers on the desk opposite. The source of their grievance is that they have received a smaller surge in their brain's reward system from their bonus because it has been depressed by the comparison with that of their colleague Sally across the desk.

The car companies' CEOs would have been acutely aware of one another's remuneration and perks, not the least of which would be access to corporate jets. Imagine if Rick had swooped into Washington in his Learjet while Alan and Robert stood waiting for the airport bus to take them to the terminal – their ventral striatums would have been limp and miserable.

So we cannot tackle the mystery of the flyers by studying them as individuals – for a more complete solution to the puzzle we need to consider the *group*.

I recently had lunch in New York with an old friend who is very senior in a US-based multi-national corporation. A gentle, clever, decent person, he would always have espoused the typically liberal outlook of his European home country. But then I asked him about Barack Obama's health-care initiative and his face darkened. I quickly said, 'I know it's a really unsatisfactory compromise but at least forty million uncovered people will now have some health protection.' His response dumbfounded me: 'They choose to spend their money on other things rather than buying health cover – that's their responsibility. I know one guy who has millions and doesn't bother to insure.'

Now here is a puzzle: how could such a highly successful, extremely intelligent person possibly believe such an argument – which he clearly did, honestly and uncynically? To think that thousands of middle-class families living in real hardship because of unemployment and house foreclosures were *choosing* to avoid paying for health insurance seemed so utterly Alice in Wonderland to me that I simply sat, open-mouthed and dazed, as the conversation meandered to other topics where my friend showed his usual intelligence and perceptiveness.

But neither my brain nor my heart was in the conversation any more. I was troubled and puzzled – how could he believe such a thing?

It was a couple of days later, when another colleague was driving me through an ice storm in upstate New York, that he gave me the answer: 'He works in a corporation where all the senior management think like that and he lives in very high end suburb – all his neighbours believe that. He works long hours and never talks to anyone who believes anything else.' Could it be as simple as that? Was his belief simply a feature of some sort of groupthink? And if so, could such groupthink help explain the riddle of the flying CEOs?

Groupthink

Jeffrey Skilling worked with two other key Enron figures: Kenneth Lay, the Chairman of the Board, and Andrew Fastow, who was Chief Financial Officer and architect of the off-books financial vehicles that hid Enron's huge losses and kept its share price artificially high. Did the fact that all three of the most senior people in the company were blind to the risks and similarly driven to push up the share price at all costs shape Skilling's strange behaviour? After all, he might have thought, 'If these smart guys think it is all right, then of course I'm right.'

Conformity is a huge factor in our behaviour, and individuals may do and tolerate almost anything if their seniors advocate or condone it. One example of this is Nazi Germany's Reserve Police Battalion 101, one of several units from Hamburg, consisting of civilians – many middle-aged and middle-class – who were sent to the newly occupied areas of eastern Europe in 1940.[34] These ostensibly respectable men, who had not been brutalised by military combat, who were under no duress and could have requested transfer from such operations without fear of sanction or criticism at any time, participated energetically in the systematic mass executions of civilians. Very few refused to take part or asked to be given other duties. Any moral compunctions they may have had – one did later report that young children refusing to leave their mothers and having to be shot together with them was a little disturbing – were extinguished by the *esprit de corps* of their units and the need for the approval of their fellow policemen and senior officers.

So was Skilling's behaviour a manifestation of that incredibly strong human need for the approval of others? Were the distorting effects of power on his thinking racked up by the support and approval of the now-jailed Fastow and the deceased Lay? They were internationally fêted winners in the business world, lauded and admired – did they all succumb to this mind-corrupting groupthink?

Except there was one who did not.

Sherron Watkins was a vice president of Enron. Her warning letter to Kenneth Lay about the accounting irregularities she had uncovered was ignored. Was it a coincidence that the only Enron whistle-blower was a woman? Would a woman have flown her corporate jet into Dulles Airport in November 2008? Was Skilling's gender one of the reasons for his downfall? Is 'winning' different for women – and are they less vulnerable to the brain-changing effects of power than men? Does the solution to the riddle of the flying CEOs lie in their gender? Strange as it may seem, to answer this question we need to solve another mystery – that of the Chinese mother.

The mystery of the Chinese mother

Please read the following words. Think about each word and consider whether it applies to you or not: *strong, dreamy, nervous, brave, curious*. If we had been scanning your brain as you did this, we would have seen that a particular part of it was very active. As we saw in Chapter 4, above your eyes, each frontal lobe of your brain curves in towards the middle of the brain – hence their name 'medial frontal lobe'. And as befits the physically interior part of your brain, this is the area that you use for mentally looking inward – for self-reflection.

Now read each of these words again – *strong, dreamy, nervous, brave, curious* – but this time ask yourself: 'Does this word [or did it, if she is deceased] apply to my mother?' A brain scan while you do that will show a neighbouring but different area becoming active. *Except*, that is, if you are Chinese or east Asian. In that case, thinking about your mother's personality will tend to activate the same parts of the brain as thinking about yourself. This is the mystery of the Chinese mother. What does it mean, and what can it tell us about the mystery of the flying CEOs?

On the morning of Thursday, 14 November 1991, Thomas McIlvane walked into the Oak Park Postal Service Office in suburban Detroit. McIlvane, recently dismissed as a postal clerk at the office, was carrying a sawn-off .22 Ruger semi-automatic carbine as he walked into the large sorting room. He pointed the gun at his former supervisors and opened fire, killing four and causing several others to injure themselves as they threw themselves from the second-storey windows in terror. McIlvane then killed himself.

The newspaper reports the next day focused understandably on McIlvane's grudge against his former employers, his dishonourable discharge from the Marines after running over a car with a tank and his generally impulsive and explosive temperament. The US Postmaster General urgently ordered that the personnel records of the Postal Service's 750,000 workers and former employees be reviewed to identify anyone who had displayed aggressive or violent behaviour.

But then other information started to trickle out.

It transpired that this office had a history of disgruntled or dismissed workers coming back to the office to fight or even on one occasion throw a telephone through the window. One *New York Times* interviewee who had worked there admitted that he himself had recently been acquitted of threatening a postal supervisor with a knife. Another man interviewed by the newspaper said that 'management pushes, pushes and pushes and doesn't know when to quit'. A third said that 'they pushed the wrong guy too far'.[35] A Congressional committee eventually concluded that McIlvane, while clearly an explosive and dangerous personality, had been harassed by managers.

Michael Morris of Stanford University and Kaiping Peng of the University of Michigan were interested in how two different newspapers covered the McIlvane shooting and another mass shooting at the University of Iowa by a Chinese physics student.[36] The first newspaper was the *New York Times* and the second was the US Chinese-language paper the *World Journal* – both internationally selling, highly reputable publications.

Morris and Peng wanted to compare how the English-speaking, non-Chinese reporters covered the two murders, in comparison with the Chinese-background, Chinese-language reporters. What they discovered showed a fundamental difference in their interpretation of events. The English-speaking journalists were much more likely to focus on McIlvane's personality, his mental instability and his short fuse, while the Chinese reporters focused much more on the *context*, such as the fact that he had recently been fired, that the postal supervisor may have been harassing him and that he may have been influenced by a recent mass shooting in Texas. The two sets of reporters showed the same sort of difference in approach to their coverage of the Chinese student's mass killing spree.

Does this tell us more about different journalistic practices across the two cultures, or is there something more fundamental going on? Morris and Peng decided to test this by asking Chinese and US students to watch short cartoons of a tank of fish. One fish was a different, blue colour from the others; sometimes it swam away from the other fish, and other times the group of fish followed it.

When asked to give an account of what had happened in each clip, the US students were much more likely to explain the scene in terms of the *internal* factors of the fish actors – factors equivalent to the personality dispositions of McIlvane that were used to explain the Oak Park shooting. Chinese students, on the other hand, were much more likely to interpret the fishy intrigue in terms of the *relationships* between the fish – equivalent to the Chinese reporter's focus on the malign work environment of the Oak Park Postal Service Office, for instance.

Individualistic cultures like those in the USA, Europe and other parts of the world not only shape people to interpret what is happening in the world very much in terms of the actions of individuals, but these differences are also reflected in the brain, with collectivist-background individuals showing evidence of a strong neural preference for processing relationships even between abstract objects.

And that brings us back to the Chinese mother.

Not only can people see *events* in these two different ways – they also see *themselves* differently. I can see *me* as a central, single *ego*, controlling my destiny and my environment. Or I can see *me* as a sort of node in a network – as a me which exists in a context, not independently of it. When Westerners think about their selves and their mothers, there is no overlap in the parts of the brain they use, but for the Chinese, their individual self is physically embedded in their brains' representation of their mothers. The Chinese self, then, is part of a greater whole, not a clear and distinct entity: this is a collectivist psychology.

Neurologically speaking, a collectivist view of the self is probably a more accurate picture than the Western individual notion. While in the West, thanks to St Bernard and his followers, we have come to give the self an almost religious significance and value, in Buddhist and Confucian thinking the self is rather a transient and changing phenomenon – in some respects it is an illusion. At the very least, 'I' do not exist outside of the network of relationships that I have with other people and if I had been brought up as a feral child with no contact with other people I would probably not have much of a 'self': 'I' exist in the reflections of the minds of the people, particularly of those who raised me.

Jeffrey Skilling did not start out as a criminal, aggressive and arrogant, if we are to believe his fellow students' comments from his college days. But power did change him, and probably, like Tony Blair, he had a high need for power. This alone, however, could not explain the Enron disaster. Skilling needed his partners Kenneth Lay and Andrew Fastow to support his skewed judgement and behaviour. But perhaps more importantly, he needed the corporate culture he created of extreme money-driven individualism to fully focus his brain on selfish gain and to blind himself to the consequences of his actions for the wider group – the Enron Corporation, its shareholders and employees. This hyper-individualist culture would have changed his brain just as the power he held did, and such a cocktail of brain-changing 'drugs' may sufficiently explain his extraordinary behaviour.

As I mentioned earlier, it would be a fair bet that Rick Wagoner, Alan Mulally and Robert Nardelli, the flying CEOs, spent a lot of time thinking about money – particularly their own bonuses and salaries, and such thoughts tend to foster self-centredness. But Wagoner, Mulally and Nardelli built *things* – automobiles – and had not turned their business into giant casinos whose only commodities were bets and bets on bets, as Enron had done. The hyper-focus on money in Enron and the possibility of huge individual profits as well as the repeated threat of culling of the individual meant that psychologically Enron was a culture that produced an extreme state of individualism. And this was even more true of much of Wall Street in the past decade.

Here then is the challenge posed by the mystery of the Chinese mother. If 'I' am a distinct, self-sufficient unit, then winning is a relatively simple business. If, on the other hand, 'I' am more of a blend – if my identity is more distributed across a group – then winning becomes a much more complicated business and throws up the challenge: *who actually wins?* From an individualist perspective, Skilling was a clear winner, up until the Enron collapse, that is. But from a collectivist perspective, he was a loser because the edifice he had created was built on financial sand and, while enriching him, impoverished many thousands of other people. In Skilling's case, the individual may have won, but the wider group lost, and exactly the same is true for many of the bankers and traders of Wall Street and the City of London.

A similar drama of the self played out in 2008, as the flying CEOs landed in Washington: their industry's downfall was primarily caused by its own failure to change, but the immediate crisis was triggered by the collapse of an inflated financial industry, in which a bonus-mediated alteration of brain function produced a culture of extreme individualism that saw some senior bank executives sacrifice their corporation's long-term viability for short-term individual financial gains.

P and S power

The question 'who wins?' only makes sense if we accept that 'I' does not really exist outside of a network of relationships with other people. Yet many of us still believe in 'I', and as we saw in the previous chapter, we seek power and status largely to find safety for that fragile 'I'. But some of us do not, and Enron's only whistle-blower was . . . a woman. Is gender a factor here?

There is a problem with such an explanation: women on average do not have any lower need for power than men, and women respond to competition and power in very similar ways to men. But there are differences: it seems that men are more power *aware* – they pay attention to signs of power more than women do, and they remember more facts about powerful than less powerful people, while women do not show this selective memory. Finally, men sniff out the power relationships in a room quicker than women do.

But still, women on average are motivated by power to the same degree as men, and so maybe gender has no relevance to what makes a winner. Perhaps Sherron Watkins's sex had nothing to do with her whistle-blowing? To help understand the role of gender in power, let's consider the speeches of two presidential hopefuls. On 3 August 2000, George W. Bush stepped out of Philadelphia's late-summer humidity into the First Union Center to accept his nomination as the Republican Party candidate to contest that year's election. Eight years later, on 28 August 2008,

Barack Obama strode out into the fresher mountain air at the Invesco Field Stadium, Denver, Colorado, to meet the applause of 84,000 people, and accept the Democratic nomination.

These two speeches were among two which a student at Rutgers University, Fatos Kusari, was to analyse in 2010 as part of his PhD thesis.[37] He was interested in the motives of US presidents and used the methods used to analyse Tony Blair and Bill Clinton's psychological make-up in Chapter 3, which were devised by the great Harvard psychologist David McLelland and his colleague David Winter, who showed that it was possible reliably to assess psychological motives 'at a distance' by analysing people's speech.

Of course, Obama and Bush would not have personally written their speeches, but they would have had a strong input and there may have been more scope for their individual personalities to emerge than would be the case once they were in presidential post.

Kusari carefully worked through the nomination acceptance speeches of these and other US presidents, coding the language to quantify the degree to which it showed evidence of three fundamental motives – for affiliation, for achievement and for power. The two presidential candidates were surprisingly similar on their affiliation – 'want to get on with others' – motive: Obama scored 59 against Bush's slightly more gregarious 63. Achievement-wise, the drive to succeed saw them roughly level-pegging too – Bush 52 against Obama's 55. But it was the third – *need for power* – that put them apart: George W. Bush's overall need for power was a high 63 while Obama's was lower but still reasonably high at 53. (John McCain's, in contrast, was only 47, and Jimmy Carter's 41.)

Historically, the higher a US president's psychological need for power, the more likely it is that that president will take the country to war, David Winter of Wesleyan University showed,[38] though so is the probability that they will be judged as a 'great' president by historians. But this difference in personal motivation between Bush and Obama, while interesting, is less relevant to the question about Sherron Watkins and Enron than was a critical fourth element of personality which Kusari assessed.

Read through the Bible's Ten Commandments below and reflect whether anything about the words springs to mind.

One: 'You shall have no other gods before Me.' Two: 'You shall not make for yourself a carved image – any likeness of anything that is in heaven above, or that is in the earth beneath, or that is in the water under the earth.' Three: 'You shall not take the name of the Lord your God in vain.' Four: 'Remember the Sabbath day, to keep it holy.' Five: 'Honour your father and your mother.' Six: 'You shall not murder.' Seven: 'You shall not commit adultery.' Eight: 'You shall not steal.' Nine: 'You shall not bear false witness against your neighbour.' Ten: 'You shall not covet your neighbour's house; you shall not covet your neighbour's wife, nor his male servant, nor his female servant, nor his ox, nor his donkey, nor anything that is your neighbour's.'

Did anything occur to you as you read through this? Glance through the list again and note how often the word 'no' or 'not' occurs. The 'religions of the book' – Christianity, Judaism and Islam – are based on sacred texts which are heavily focused on limits on behaviour, on moral codes about what and what is not acceptable. They also focus on individuals submitting to the higher authority of religious law. Finally, there is a concentration on the responsibility of the individual for upholding sacred law – underpinned by a strong sense in which a person's individual appetites should be suppressed in favour of the greater good.

There is, in other words, a very strong cultural and historical tradition of inhibition – of saying no to certain impulses – which is inculcated century after century into the minds of millions of people. David McClelland, in making this observation, noticed that this sense of responsibility and of suppressing individual cravings for a greater good, played itself out in the language of some people who had a high need for power.[39] And it did so in a very simple way – in how often words like 'not' and others ending in 'n't' arose in the speech and thoughts of people who shared a high need for power and influence over other people.

McClelland characterised the two types of power need as *p-power* – power need for personal goals – and *s-power* – power need focused on goals for an institution, a group or a society. He noted that when they wrote short stories, p-power-predominant individuals tended to portray life as a 'zero sum game' in which 'I win or you lose', and vice versa. Their need to have an impact tended to be satisfied assertively, with a strong drive to beat the opponent and win the contest, in comparison with the s-power-predominant person, who was more driven to achieve a change for some wider benefit than just the high of winning: in particular, the high s-power person tends to feel some moral or legal standard governing his or her behaviour, and along with that is a sense of obligation and a concern for others. There is also a concern about consequences underpinning their need for power, and a degree of self-judgement, through which they critically examine their own character, self-control and good sense.

The Rutgers PhD student Fatos Kusari applied McClelland's analysis of George W. Bush's and Barack Obama's speeches – deriving an index of what McClelland called 'activity inhibition'. While Kusari found that Bush and Obama were both pretty power-needy people, their scores on an underlying sense of inhibition and responsibility diverged sharply. Obama scored a high 65 on the inhibition measure, while Bush only scored

40. Obama's high need for power included more of the s-power variety, while Bush's included more of the p-power.

As an interesting aside, David McClelland had discovered that heavy drinkers tended to have a high need for power – something that should not be surprising given the dopamine hunger that underpins drugs, power, money and sex. But he also discovered that a high s-power index seemed to help prevent high-power needy people from falling into heavy drinking patterns.[40] George W. Bush had well-documented problems with alcohol before becoming president, while this is not the case for Barack Obama.

But lest it appear that s-power motivation is the prerogative of the Democratic Party and p-power of the Republicans, Kusari's data shows that this is not the case. The Republican candidate John McCain, for instance, scored higher than Barack Obama on the s-power-related measure of activity inhibition, while the Democratic President Jimmy Carter scored the same as George W. Bush.

It still tightens my stomach to think of walking to school that day in October 1962 when it looked like the world was going to end: I can remember vividly the grainy black and white U2 aircraft reconnaissance photographs of the ballistic missiles in Cuba, and the television footage of US warships surging alongside Soviet freighters. With nuclear weapons already airborne on US bombers, the sentient world was paralysed with fear. In the end Chairman Khrushchev backed down and John F. Kennedy's steely but nevertheless cautious strategy was vindicated.

John Magee of New York University and colleagues replayed this crisis with a group of students and staff of a US East Coast university.[41] Nearly fifty years after that awful October day, most of the participants in this study had no personal memory of it.

They were given briefing papers about the course of events and were then presented with a list of precisely those policy options which President Kennedy would have been given.

The options that Magee presented to the participants were as follows: 'a) Ignore Khrushchev, bomb the missile bases, and launch a full-scale US invasion to remove all offensive weapons and overthrow the Castro regime. 2. Ignore Khrushchev, and bomb the missile bases. 3. Ignore Khrushchev, and tighten the US blockade to include oil. 4. Ignore Khrushchev, leave the US blockade as it is, and wait. 5. Leave the US blockade as it is, but offer to negotiate with Khrushchev on the basis of his proposals. 6. Call off the blockade, and offer to negotiate with Khrushchev on the basis of his proposals. 7. Accept Khrushchev's proposals as they stand, and call off the blockade.'

The participants then ranked these options in terms of what they would have advised President Kennedy to do. Magee and his colleague Carrie Langner then asked four questions about the extent they would advise the president to *deliberate* over the chosen policy response. They asked them the following questions: 'To what extent is it advisable to defer the decision about how to respond until further evidence can be collected?' (1 = not at all; 9 = extremely), 'How quickly would you advise the President to make his decision?' (1 = not at all; 9 = extremely), 'To what extent is it advisable to seize the opportunity to respond now?' (1 = not at all; 9 = extremely), and 'To what extent should the decision about how to respond be expedited?' (1 = not at all; 9 = very much).

Magee then rated their participants on their levels of p versus s power: they discovered that the higher the level of p power, the more likely they were to advise the president to escalate the responses; what's more, the higher their level of p power, the less they would have advised the president to deliberate before triggering a particular policy. A high p-power president, in other words, might have tipped the world into nuclear Armageddon. It seems a reasonable hypothesis that the financial near-Armageddon of 2008 may have been driven by a group of people with a higher average p power than President Kennedy and his advisers had.

It may seem a long way from the Ten Commandments to the intricate operation of the human brain, but they are closer than we might think.

Imagine this: you volunteer for a psychology experiment where you are paired up with a stranger and told you are trying to beat him in how fast you can connect the numbers in a number grid. Whoever finishes first has to say 'Done!' and the other person has to stop at once. If you imagine this properly, you may feel your muscles tense and your eyes narrow at the prospect of the contest and your testosterone levels will rise.

Now the contest begins. If you are a competitive person, you know that you will really go at it – trying to beat the other person because that's the way you are – competitive. You are going really well when your heart jumps as your partner triumphantly shouts 'Done!' and slams down his pencil. Damn!

But what you don't know is that the contest is *rigged*. You and your partner have been randomly assigned to an easier and a harder number grid so that he was destined to win no matter how hard you competed. The same was true for all the other pairs. Pretty unfair, but what was the point?

The point was that Oliver Schultheiss of the University of Michigan had measured the levels of p and s power in the volunteers before the contest.[42] It's worth remembering that it's not a question of whether a participant was a p- *or* an s-power person – most of us have a bit of *both* types of motivation. The more p power you have, the more you tend to satisfy your burning need for impact in assertive ways, and the more s power you have, the more you satisfy your big need for impact through altruistic routes – but most people have a bit of both. Teachers and nurses, for instance, have a high need for power, but they tend to be much higher on the s type than p power, while politicians and policemen tend to be higher on p power.

But if these slightly vague psychological descriptions really are central to understanding the flying CEOs, the Enron fiasco and Wall Street madness, there really should be some more *tangible* manifestation of the s versus p power distinction, shouldn't there? – for instance, in the actions that Sherron Watkins took when she discovered the irregular accounting practices.

This is precisely what Oliver Schultheiss found: after the number-grid contest – the men with the highest p-power levels had the largest rise in testosterone in just imagining winning the contest before actually taking part, and the levels stayed high after actually 'winning': not surprisingly, these highly competitive p-power men didn't maintain the high testosterone levels after doing something they really did not like to do – *lose*.

But things started to get really interesting when the scientists compared men with and without s-power motivation: they still had varying degrees of p- power drive, but some *also* had s-power motivation. In the men with *absent* s power, just imagining winning the contest before actually taking part gave them double the testosterone levels of men who also had some s-power motivation: fantasies of domination, in other words, really got these p-power-only men going.

And when they *won*, the p-power-only men's testosterone kept flowing. But when they lost, it fell. The picture for men with both p power *and* s- power couldn't have been more different. Not only did their juices flow less freely when fantasising about winning the contest, but there was no longer a relationship between how much p power they had and how much testosterone flowed in response to the dominance fantasy.

Things were even more interesting after the contest. In the men with both p and s power, the more p power they had, the *less* their testosterone surged after winning. The mere presence of a bit of s-power motivation in the minds of these men, in other words, *reduced* the dominance-testosterone link that all men have. The p- and s-power men still had a strong drive for impact, both personally and socially, but compared with men who *only* had the personal power drive, they did not 'get off' on winning a pretty trivial and meaningless contest against a stranger.

In conclusion: s power *tames* p power.

But does this help us answer whether Sherron Watkins's gender helped her escape the deranged groupthink of the most senior Enron executives?

Research by Leonard Chusmir and Barbara Parker of the University of Colorado suggests that it does.[43] Comparing p power in men and women, they found that women were on average as motivated as men to have an assertive, personal impact on other people. But when it came to s power – the need to have impact driven by altruistic reasons – women were significantly higher in s power than men. Women, in other words, were more motivated than men to control others for the wider benefit of the community or organisation, not just for themselves.

S power not only tames p power – it also dissolves p power's physiological linkage to testosterone and the competitive aggression that goes with it. S power acts as a sort of coolant on the potent but sometimes destructive effects of unmitigated p power, and women's minds have more of this coolant. What's more, s power's dissolving effects on testosterone very probably diminish the most virulent of the dopamine surges that can lead to addiction to power: this may be one reason why all the notorious and massacring dictators of the world have been men.

But it is not simply a question of gender. Many women have high p power undiminished by s power, and conversely, many men have high levels of s power. Both show surges in testosterone when faced with a contest, and both have an equal average level of desire to have an impact on other people.

The collapse of Enron can thus be explained like this: a group of p-power-driven people – mainly men – whose testosterone levels were racked up by repeated market 'successes' of an escalating share price, created and lived in a culture of extreme 'millionaire factory' individualism. The combination of money-primed individualism, judgement skewed by testosterone-triggered dopamine and risk perception dulled by the biological consequences of the winner effect meant that their attention was focused on narrow goals – overwhelmingly the share price at the expense of any real consideration of the actual business of supplying energy. Their moral judgement was dulled by power, which also made them more vulnerable to applying different standards of conduct to themselves than they did to others. The absence of s-power 'coolant' in their psychology means that their brains were exposed to much higher levels of raw testosterone – and hence to repeated surges of dopamine coursing through the reward parts of their brain.

The riddle of the flying CEOs may be explained by a subset of these factors. Self-interest would have been triggered by enormous performance bonuses and the concurrent isolating privileges; the neurological effects of considerable power may have made them less able to see things from other people's point of view, in particular the perspective of the population on that day in Washington. The gung-ho, reward-seeking, *approach* parts of their brains may have been fired up by a power-induced goal focus, and the more cautious, vigilant, *avoidance* brain areas correspondingly less active. They would have felt sharp and mentally on top of their game, but power had sharpened only some parts of their brains – and may have dulled others: hence their judgement was sufficiently skewed as to render them surprised by the public anger at their transport arrangements on 18 November 2008.

As in Enron, there was only a small number of senior female executives in their companies; had there been more women, their likely higher-than-average levels of s-power motivation would have meant they would have had brains less affected by testosterone and its brain-changing by-product, dopamine. Who knows whether Enron would have imploded if there had been more women on the board, but it is almost certain that the Enron bubble would not have been created had the company been staffed with more people with higher levels of s power, whatever their gender.

But does this help us? Power's effects on the brains of Skilling, Lay and Fastow – men with high levels of power need whose brains were affected by power and money in a self-interested casino where the common good was swept away in a tide of greed – was mirrored in other companies eight years later and contributed to the near-collapse of the world's financial system.

During the Libyan uprising of early 2011 the country's leader the late Muammar Gaddafi and his son Saif appeared on television, making wide-eyed threats to annihilate the 'terrorists' who had had the temerity to protest on the streets against a toxic dictatorship. Both father and son appeared drugged and incoherent, but the pharmaceutical agent which may have caused this strange, pupil-dilated ranting was generated in their own bodies: likely huge surges of testosterone triggered waves of dopamine in the ventral striatum of their brains, causing an extreme version of the blinkered and delusional state that Jeffrey Skilling showed. And they thought of themselves as winners.

In the final chapter I will turn the spotlight on the winner's mind and what winning actually means.

6

The Winning Mind

We have solved the five mysteries and along the way have uncovered the many ways in which we are shaped by power, for good or for bad. In this chapter our challenge is to try to understand how these help us understand what it is that makes a winner. But first we have to consider what it actually means to be a 'winner'.

We were sitting round a crackling fire in a country cottage, a group of house guests and their hosts relaxing after a winter walk. We relaxed into the chat between new acquaintances, but within an hour the conversation seemed to die out as we all noticed the interaction between two of the guests. It was somehow like the rest of us weren't there as one of the women acted almost if she were alone in the room with the forlorn-looking man, who, with downcast eyes, was already sinking another whisky.

If this had been a workplace she wouldn't have stood a chance with her harassment, bullying, mental cruelty – any judge or tribunal would have nailed her. It was a ruthless public humiliation in front of strangers, a systematic dismantling of the man's qualities, both personal and professional, his looks, his social and intellectual inadequacy – and yes, even thirty years later I feel excruciating embarrassment at the memory – there were oblique hints of sexual incompetence too.

And this man was her husband.

'Chris' – not his real name – took it like a whipped dog. And the more he took it, the more strangely enlivened she looked: her eyes glittered, her voice rose and her viciousness deepened. She exuded triumph and something much worse – *contempt*.

Whatever the battle she was fighting, 'Karen' – not her real name – was clearly the winner of this contest: her whole bright-eyed demeanour was that of the victor, like a gladiator occasionally glancing around at us as if we were emperors expected to give the thumbs up or down to this poor loser's emotional life.

John Gottman is the world's expert on relationships and marital break-up. His research has shown that the presence of contempt in the speech or demeanour of one marital partner is a sign that the relationship is doomed.[1] But where does it come from, this contempt – what fuels its malign energy? A story about a phone call to my house will help answer this question.

The voice on the line said that they were carrying out a health survey consisting of a single, innocuous question: 'Does anyone in your household suffer from asthma?'

'Yes,' I said.

'Well, we would like to offer you the chance to watch a short video about asthma. If you agree, we can offer you and your family free holiday flights.'

'We just have to watch a video? How long is it?'

'Just half an hour. When can we send someone?'

It was a beautiful summer morning when the man arrived at the door. Only half an hour and we'd be able to take the children swimming at Cambridge's lovely if unheated outdoor swimming pool.

'I just have to get a few things out of the car,' he said.

We watched as he lugged some equipment up the stairs to our living room. Obviously a pretty advanced video projection set-up, I thought to myself.

He pulled out a large glossy folder with lavish colour photo-graphs of revolting-looking mites that live in house dust and are a major source of allergy asthma.

'What about the video?' I asked.

'Oh, that is an old video – what I'll show you is much more relevant – but I can get it out of the car for you if you want?'

'How long is this going to take? You said it would be half an hour.'

'It won't take a moment to show you this.'

Within a few minutes he had spilled a pile of sandy dirt on our cream-coloured carpet and we were, of course, annoyed. Moments later the super-powerful, asthma-beating vacuum device had sucked up the demo dirt and before we knew it he was in our bedroom, assembling some other piece of asthma technology.

'You said half an hour – it has been over an hour now,' I reminded him.

He was expertly putting together some large device, not replying.

'Please leave now.'

'It won't take long . . .'

'Leave now, please, we don't want to see more, and we don't want to buy it.'

'But . . .'

'We are going out. Leave.'

Reluctantly and grumpily he lugged his equipment and glossy books down the stairs into his car. I heard him on the telephone to his office, saying that he had only managed to do half a demonstration.

*   *   *

The salesman had skilfully controlled our responses using well-worn technologies of human influence.

It started with a 'yes'. The moment you answer yes to a cold caller, they have a hook into you. The 'yes' in this case was to the question 'Does anyone in your household suffer from asthma?' but it could have been to any question. That 'yes' – or indeed any reasonably positive response to the caller – automatically makes it more difficult to say no later on. This is the mental 'foot in the door' that salespeople are so adept at inserting.

Let's take a familiar office scenario. Suppose you covet the desk of a colleague – perhaps one with more light and a better view. She spends half the week out of the office while you are there all week, so there is a certain logic to a swap. But it is her desk, you know she doesn't really like you very much and there is no pressure for her to yield to this weak logic. How do you persuade her to change desks?

The solution to this problem lies in what has been called the 'Ben Franklin effect'. The eighteenth-century American founding father, polymath and politician had problems with the animosity of a rival Pennsylvania legislator who was a sort of Sarah Palin to Franklin's Barack Obama. This legislator's enmity was causing the great man difficulties, so how could he bring him round? Anticipating the sales techniques and cognitive science of three centuries later, the clever Franklin did something quite unexpected – he asked his rival for a favour.

Franklin knew that the man had a rare book in his library, so he asked him if he could borrow it for a few days. He returned it a week later with a note of thanks. In his autobiography, Franklin reports with satisfaction how when they next met, his rival spoke to him for the first time in a civil and even friendly way. He went on to offer Franklin any other help he needed and gradually their relationship flowered into a friendship that lasted throughout their lives.

So, back to that coveted desk with the nice view of the river – you now know what to do to get it. First, ask your colleague for a small favour – like lending you a pencil. Perhaps later you can ask her for a few small coins to make up the price of a coffee from the machine. Once you have created this disposition to say yes and do things for you, she will be much more likely to agree to the logic of swapping desks.

We may not realise it, but our thoughts, feelings and behaviour are controlled by other people every day using simple techniques like this. Robert Cialdini describes these in his classic book *The Psychology of Influence and Persuasion*.[2]

But what has this question of influence got to do with our troubled house guests Karen and Chris?

Have you ever done something absent-minded like throw the peeled potato into the bin and the peelings into the pot, sent an email saying there is a document attached without actually attaching the document or slipped up in some similar way? Everyday mistakes like these happen all the time because our brains have to keep track of hundreds of different responses to thousands of different potential stimuli every hour of our waking lives. Even though a second earlier we wrote that we were attaching a document to the email, the very next second our brain fires off a command to our fingers to send the attachment-less email – and sometimes we don't even realise our mistake until we get an email from the addressee pointing it out.

If you had the job of designing a brain from scratch, pretty soon you would work out that you needed some sort of device which looked out for mistakes like this – a sort of error watchman. If you don't build in such a mechanism, our brains would

get into all sorts of scrapes; that is why we have evolved a structure deep in the middle of the front half of our brains called the
anterior cingulate cortex (ACC), part of whose job is to ring
neural bells when we make mistakes.

But what has this got to do with salesmen and warring couples?
The answer follows from the fact that the ACC does more than
just detect mistakes when they happen. More generally it acts
as the brain's conflict detector, identifying potential contradictory impulses in the brain that may lead to costly mistakes, as
research in my laboratory also showed.[3] What do I mean by
conflict? Take this example: you are driving down a road and see
that the traffic light ahead has been green for quite a long time.
Two possible conflicting courses of action hatch in your brain:
either you can keep on driving at your present speed, maybe
even recklessly speeding up a little to beat the light, or you can
anticipate a traffic-light change and begin to slow down, ready
to stop. These are two totally opposite impulses simultaneously
active in your brain and they have to be sorted out very quickly
to avoid an accident.

Here is another example of the brain at war with itself. You
are tired and looking forward to a quiet half-hour reading the
newspaper in a coffee shop when, your coffee and paper in hand,
you see an old colleague just ahead of you about to sit down
at a table. Just as in the traffic lights case, your brain is faced
with quickly resolving two opposite and incompatible actions:
a cheery 'hello' to the old colleague, who you know will be
delighted to see you, or a quick retreat into a dark corner secretly
to enjoy your peaceful moment.

In both of these cases the ACC would be working overtime,
signalling conflicting responses – the equivalent of an error as
far as the brain is concerned – and, with the help of other parts
of the brain, particularly the frontal lobes, quickly resolving the

conflict. If it doesn't, you could end up with a dangerous mix of responses such as accelerating wildly then screeching to a halt at the lights, or turning away too late, clumsily spilling your coffee and attracting the attention of the colleague you are trying to avoid to your embarrassing avoidance moves.

The brain is the most complicated entity in the known universe and consists of many different parts working mostly unconsciously but – we hope – in a reasonably co-ordinated way. But there is too much going on for there to be guaranteed harmony, which is why we are bundles of often contradictory impulses: 'I really want to have this drink but I know I shouldn't.' 'Boy, I would like to tell him what an obnoxious creep he is, but it could rebound on me' and so on. But while we have lots of these contradictory impulses, most of us, most of the time, manage to behave reasonably consistently, and we demand of one another a veneer of consistency – the comforting notion that there is a sensible, square-jawed pilot – let's call it the *ego* – in each of our skulls, calmly navigating us through life.

But the human beings surrounding us are far too complicated to let the pilot go about its business calmly and rationally. Different people ask sometimes incompatible things of us – partners, workmates, friends, bosses – or make what are often contradictory demands on us. Conflict is, in other words, almost inevitably created in our brains by the complexities of our relationships. And so there must be some way of managing these contradictory demands.

Vincent van Veen and his colleagues from the University of California at Berkeley created conflict in the minds of volunteers while they were still lying there after doing an uncomfortable and terribly boring forty-five-minute task in the narrow, claustrophobic and very noisy tube of an MRI scanner. They did this by telling the volunteers that a patient was waiting to be scanned and was quite apprehensive about undergoing what was a medically important scan. The researchers asked if the participant in the scanner could reassure the nervous patient that it was actually quite pleasant inside the scanner. The volunteers would help the patient by making a rating of pleasantness that they were told the patient could see in a screen in the waiting room and to cast it in a positive light, in spite of how they actually felt about it. In other words, the participants were asked to lie about their true feelings, for the purpose of helping the patient. Of course there was no patient, but the volunteers believed there was, and dutifully concealed their feelings, having just revealed their true negative feelings about the scanner experience to the researchers. The volunteers, in other words, were being asked to declare a belief that ran opposite to their actual feelings.

So here we have the type of situation all of us face from time to time – having to juggle the demands of other people and conceal our true feelings for other people's benefit. This study provides a specific example of a situation where opposite impulses are simultaneously triggered in the brain – of feeling negative about the scanning on the one hand, while expressing positive feelings about it on the other. In the earlier real-life examples of conflicting impulses – approaching the traffic light that has been green for a long time, or avoiding the workmate in the café – these are the conflict-balancing processes going on in the brain.

Van Veen and his colleagues discovered that a particular part of the ACC called the dorsal ACC (dACC) was involved in resolving the conflict. This part of the brain surged into life like an alarm detecting a burglar. So far so good. However, the Berkeley researchers discovered something else quite strange. But before I tell you what it was, and before we go back to Karen and Chris, let's recall a famous kidnapping.

Heiress with a gun

In an iconic image of the 1970s, the San Francisco publishing heiress Patty Hearst is caught on CCTV wielding a heavy-calibre gun while robbing a bank. This photograph was taken just a few months after she had been kidnapped from her home, locked for weeks in a tiny, lightless closet, repeatedly raped and threatened with execution by a small self-styled group of would-be political criminals called the Symbionese Liberation Army. How did Hearst – or Tania as she now called herself – end up robbing a bank for her rapists, when she could have as easily turned her gun on them?

After she was eventually captured and prosecuted for armed robbery, the court rejected her defence of brainwashing and threw her into prison for seven years. She had declared in broadcast tapes before her capture that she was acting of her free will and the judge and jury took her at her word. President Jimmy Carter commuted the sentence, and President Bill Clinton eventually pardoned her. Hearst/Tania was a classic case of the 'Stockholm Syndrome', where hostages bond emotionally with their kidnappers. Forty years later, across the chilly waters of San Francisco Bay in Berkeley, van Veen and his team helped uncover what may have been going on in Patty Hearst's – or was it Tania's? – brain.

What happened when people argued against their own strongly held attitudes? van Veen wondered. How did the brain manage the conflict of arguing that the MRI scanner experience was pleasant when actually the volunteers were bored and uncomfortable? Cognitive dissonance – which I discussed in Chapter 5 – also comes into play here. True to the research of the great social psychologist Leon Festinger, van Veen discovered that the volunteers who lied to the patient about how pleasant it

was inside the scanner actually ended up feeling that the experience *had* been more pleasant once they were out of the scanner.

Festinger recognised that we have a really strong need to
keep our unruly brains, with their hundreds of contradictory
impulses, under some sort of discipline. He proposed that we
have a very strong drive to maintain a consistency that will help
preserve the sanity of the ego. His theory of cognitive dissonance
proposed that we are powerfully motivated to maintain consistency in our thoughts, feelings and actions – in other words to
minimise conflict among them. Van Veen created conflict in the
minds of his public-spirited volunteers by asking them to lie to
a fictitious patient about how pleasant it had been inside the
scanner. This sort of inconsistency, Festinger had proposed, set
up a very uncomfortable conflict in the minds of these consistency-loving people and the dACC went into overdrive to try to
resolve it.

But how did these individuals actually resolve it? They did
so by unconsciously changing how they actually felt about the
experience. 'Actually, it wasn't too bad, you know?' would have
been the sort of thing they said to themselves and to the researchers after it finished. Those who hadn't been asked to lie to help
the fictitious anxious patient realistically rated the experience
as relatively unpleasant, in contrast with the dissonance-inflated
positive ratings given by their conflicted fellow participants. Van
Veen showed that the more the volunteers positively changed
their real attitude to scanning, the more the dACC was active.
The brain's conflict watchdog had done a really good job in these
cases – rapidly sorting out the uncomfortable inconsistency in
the minds of these conscientious participants by the simple
expedient of changing how they felt about the experience.

When someone is kidnapped and abused, they are faced with
a dilemma – do they continue to resist or do they try to make

life more tolerable by trying to appease or even befriend the captors? People caught in such a situation and who choose the latter course should beware. Like van Veen's volunteers, they will set their dorsal anterior cingulate cortex into overdrive because of the inconsistency between the nice way they are behaving towards the captors on the one hand, and their feelings of anger, fear and resentment towards them on the other.

And the harder the dACC works, the better it will reduce uncomfortable cognitive dissonance. And how does it reduce it? By changing their true feelings towards the kidnappers. We can't know for certain, but it is very likely that something like that went on in Patty Hearst's brain. She was brainwashed into a devotion for the 'cause' of a group of unstable criminals who had kidnapped her, all to banish uncomfortable cognitive dissonance.

And so it is for your unsuspecting colleague with that lovely desk. She has given you a pencil and lent you money. Once she has done these things for you, you have set up a conflict in her mind and switched on her dACC: she didn't like you much in the past but she has found herself doing all these things for you and so her dACC works overtime to resolve this by applying the Ben Franklin effect and changing how she feels about you.

Now you can move in like a salesman making the closing move for the sale and ask her, 'Since you are only here some of the time, would you mind if we swapped desks?' What can she say? 'You're a nice colleague, aren't you (you must be if I have done all these things for you, her dACC mutters), and I'm here only half the time – so of course I'll swap.' Bingo. That's what the asthma salesman traded off as well – that dACC which was working overtime sorting out the conflict between 'I've just let this stranger into my living room and bedroom, allowed him to set up machinery, spill dirt on my carpet and keep me from the swimming pool on a sunny summer morning' and 'Boy, this stuff must be really special!'

I found it really difficult to come to the point where I asked the salesman to leave – it felt like a struggle, which is exactly what it was – a struggle against the powerful conflict resolution that the dACC was exerting on my thoughts and emotions.

And now we are back to Karen and Chris and their strange interactions. Where did her *contempt* come from? Quite simply, it emerged from the power that she had over him. Power is having control over the things that other people need and want . . . and also over what they fear. Chris loved Karen, it seemed, at least superficially, to us, and she had control over the thing that he wanted most – her affection. She also had control over the thing he feared most – abandonment by her. From the narrow perspective of this unhealthy relationship, she was a *winner*.

So Karen had this considerable emotional power over Chris – but why should that make her feel contempt for him? We saw in the previous chapter that power over someone makes the powerful more inclined to treat that person as an object. Objects don't have free will and don't make decisions, and it is the belief – often justified – of power holders that their under-lings' behaviour is under their control. This sort of power snuffs out empathy – how can we have empathy for an object?

It was clear that Karen had no empathy for Chris's humiliation and misery – if anything she seemed to be revelling in it. She was playing with him like a cat with a squirming mouse. But lack of empathy, even cruelty, doesn't equate with contempt. Where did that come from? It's probably obvious by now that the dACC is going to come into play here. If my emotional power over you inclines me to see you as an object under my control, then it is inevitable that my behaviour towards you will deteriorate, in the absence of empathy as a corrective. But as I observe my behaviour towards you deteriorating, my consistency-loving brain detects a jarring conflict between my poor behaviour on the one hand, and the ego's need for a positive self-image on the other.

And so a sort of reverse Ben Franklin effect comes into play to create a sort of corrupted form of 'winning': 'If I am behaving like this towards you, then you must be a really unappealing person' is the contorted logic that the dACC squeezes into our brain in the service of our overwhelming need for consistency. But here is the really awful part of all this: remember how Benjamin Franklin made a friend of his enemy by getting him to lend him his rare book? What would have happened if he had goaded his rival into doing something bad to him – for instance, stealing something of Franklin's? The logic is clear: the rival would then be *more likely to do something bad – probably even worse – to Franklin again.* And that rationalisation would give him the satisfaction of the winner – 'Ha! I showed him.'

The bully as winner

This is the logic of cognitive dissonance – that strange need to keep the ego reassured that what is being done is all right and proper and above all *consistent*. This is, of course, how bullies work. They pick a victim. They then choose someone in the group who has no strong feelings about the victim, or maybe even likes them. The bully then gets that person to do some small tease or trick on the person – something which on its own is trivial, perhaps even mildly funny, like hiding a bag or putting some slightly embarrassing object on their desk.

This is, of course, the negative equivalent of you asking your colleague for a pencil. In getting the confederate to play the trick, you are getting from them a commitment which, because of cognitive dissonance, means that they will find it hard to say no when the bully asks them to do something a little bit less innocent. The dACC quickly detects conflict in the bully's new companion's brain: 'I'm a good person, but I am doing this to them – ergo, they must be a bad person deserving of this.'

And so we see spiralling situations where more and more people in a group are manipulated by the bully into harassing and mobbing the poor victim – all using the Ben Franklin effect. Most of them in other circumstances may be decent people but unbeknown to them, the bully has injected conflict into their inconsistency-hating brains, forcing the dACC to desperately balance out the conflict in the only way it can – by concluding that the victim is hateful and deserving of all they are getting.

But this is not a static situation: remember how Ben Franklin's rival didn't just become more positively disposed to Franklin after lending him his book, but he wanted to do *more* – to do *better* things for Franklin, to the point where they eventually became lifelong friends. The awful reality for the victim of bullying is that there is an equivalent toxic escalation of *worse* things that happen in the brain's balancing out of internal conflict: 'If she is that bad, then she must deserve something even worse' and so on. But keeping the ego calm by dampening down conflict in the brain isn't the only thing going on in the minds of a bullying group. There is, of course, one other potent mechanism, a drug no less – *power*.

And what better drug could there be for a self-doubting, bored, mixed-up teenager? It doesn't matter that the goal that power focuses you on is twisting the cord of mental anguish round a classmate whom you maybe even quite liked just a few days previously. But power is a drug that floods our brains with potentially addictive chemicals and, like all drugs, it can take a strong hold on people. Every so often a story hits the press where a victim – often a teenager in a school – has committed suicide after a campaign of bullying. The report almost always uncovers a steady escalation of harassment and usually describes the resulting distress of many of the erstwhile bullies as well.

The T cichlid fish is also a bully in his Lake Tanganyika school playground. But this is not because he is born a dominant bully, or has some individual personality disorder leading him to behave this way. No, his behaviour is a result of circumstance – of his being lucky enough to get territory, and this status then transforms him physically and psychologically. That is why too much focus on the individual psychology of the bullying group can often be fruitless: yes, of course there can be a psychologically disturbed or slightly sociopathic individual who uses these Ben Franklin sales techniques to trick psychologically normal classmates or workmates into joining the mob. But the mob process itself is accelerated by their individual brains being intoxicated by power and changed by constant dACC-initiated rationalisation of their behaviour.

And so it was for Karen. She wasn't a psychologically disturbed person, prone to cruelty throughout her life. No, she and her husband had descended into a situation where she held all the cards in their relationship. Karen had total emotional power and that power began to corrupt her into believing she was a winner in this strange emotional battle that we witnessed. Chris, of course, began to show the symptoms of extreme powerlessness – passivity, loss of initiative, depression, low self-esteem, fearfulness – which is not an attractive package for any partner, male or female – nobody loves a loser. The power that Karen held made her reckless and unempathic in her behaviour towards Chris, and his whipped-dog retreat into defencelessness and drinking simply confirmed the stance that her dACC was taking in the brain, rationalising her extraordinary behaviour by seeing him as a really pathetic, disgusting person. And that is where the contempt came from.

But contempt is not just a symptom of a sick marriage – it can be a warning sign that a leader is becoming affected by power. The German Chancellor Angela Merkel unsuccessfully tried to persuade the then Russian President Vladimir Putin that he should not express contempt for his cabinet ministers, as he habitually did in the presence of fellow world leaders, Tony Blair's former Chief of Staff Jonathan Powell recalls in his book *The New Machiavelli – How to Wield Power in the Modern World*. Powell describes Putin's cichlid-fish-like transformation from highly intelligent and apparently reasonable statesman to hubristic and power-intoxicated Tsar-like figure as his grip on presidential power strengthened.

They were a vibrant couple, arguing good-naturedly over what music to put on and laughing when he almost let the main course burn. She patted his head mock-patronisingly, consoling him for his absent-mindedness; he smiled and told her that at least he was good at choosing the wine. She nodded and took a sip from her glass.

It was the first time I had seen him for at least two years, a chance encounter at the home of mutual friends, and I stole a wondering glance at him – Chris looked so incredibly happy. Not only happy, but strong and confident. His demeanour had changed beyond recognition – it was as if he had had a personality transplant – which in a way, he had.

Funnily enough, I bumped into Karen not long after: she and Ken were living together and it was intriguing to see her holding his arm and glancing up at him almost coyly as she we swapped catch-up stories. Another personality transplant? Well, yes. It's not that personality is totally malleable: we saw earlier how deep motivational drives embedded in our personality – pressing needs for achievement or power, for instance – do differentiate us, as well as other personality characteristics such as extraversion-introversion, neuroticism-stability and several others. These features of our personality are only dispositions to behave in a certain way, however. It is only those of us who have let ourselves be put under the curse of genetic fatalism who consider ourselves imprisoned by a supposedly immutable personality. The relationships we have with people around us – particularly partners, but also workmates, politicians, police, administrators, teachers, classmates, relatives and friends – also shape our personalities to an enormous extent.

Karen and Chris were like the dramatically changing cichlid fish of Chapter 2, each changed colour, physiology and behaviour to an unrecognisable degree – not by medical intervention, but rather by changing their partners. But the effects of such a simple change in circumstance transformed them more completely than a medical intervention could: Chris's brain would have changed enormously, his memory improving as cortisol levels in his blood subsided, and his initiative and confidence surging with increased testosterone and brain dopamine levels. He would have become smarter, more focused, less anxious and less risk-averse – all because he was no longer powerless.

Karen would also have changed – less dopamine and testosterone with her reduced power, but instead more empathy, and maybe a little more anxiety and worry about the future. True, her eyes no longer had the glitter of a triumphant winner, and she had lost that predatory, gladiatorial edge, but she seemed, well, happier. It wasn't that she was now subservient to her new partner – far from it, as I found out later, they were a feisty couple subject to the usual power tussles of any relationship.

Like Chris's new partnership, it was a balance of power, a give and take with neither party particularly dominant. This was a different sort of winning.

I am not advocating relationship-hopping to find the ideal partner. Our personalities may be shaped by our current relationships as Karen and Chris's were, but we also bring our own motivational baggage into relationships: Chris had a disposition to passivity and would have tended to attract and be attracted to women who had a disposition to be dominant. Karen had a disposition to be dominant and would have unconsciously sought out men she would feel able to control.

Karen and Chris could easily have ended up in a succession of repeated winner–loser relationships like the one theirs had become. As that weekend in the country too clearly showed, their relationship was irretrievable, but who knows what might have been possible earlier in the downward spiral before each of their brains and personalities had been re-engineered by the unequal levels of power in their relationship.

It may seem strange to choose an example of female-on-male abuse when worldwide many more women are victims of unequal power than men are. Men are not in many countries systematically deprived of the human rights of education, relationships and work by political and religious systems because of their gender, but women are. The resulting powerlessness of hundreds of millions of women fundamentally shapes their brains, reducing their capacity to change their situation.

I chose Karen and Chris because it made the cichlid-fish story of their behaviour easier to tell than if it had been a male-on-female abuse story. Had it been a tale of Chris publicly humiliating Karen, it would have unconsciously primed in our minds caveman-type images of males inevitably dominating women because of inherited biological drives over which they have no control – the curse of genetic fatalism would have distorted our thinking, in other words. But the cichlid fish, rather than the caveman, is the more appropriate story. Whether we like it or not, power is at the heart of all our relationships. It is impossible to have a meaningful relationship with someone without having some power over that person, and that person must also have some power over you.

Power is having control over things that the other needs, wants or fears. Every relationship with any substance involves attention, affection and threat of rejection – among many other things – being dispensed with varying degrees of equality. When power becomes unbalanced, people change physically and mentally, and in extreme cases this can cause Jekyll and Hyde-like transformations. When, as with Karen and Chris, the power imbalance becomes extreme, then people can become corrupted by – and sometimes addicted to – that power. But it is not just in adult partnerships that power is so central.

Mama! Papa! We shall overthrow your power!

Children in the Soviet Union of the 1920s had a limited range of entertainment and hence the children's publication *Murzilka* was very widely read. On the cover of one edition of that era was emblazoned 'Mama! Papa! We shall overthrow your power!' in strident italic capitals. The Soviet Communist Party had shouldered its way into the middle of the most fundamental of all power struggles in mankind's history – that between parent and child.

The need for autonomy – along with the need for human

companionship – is one of the most fundamental of human requirements. Anyone who has lived through their children's 'terrible twos' stage of development will have seen this ancient power struggle at first hand. 'No!' – that emblem of opposition to someone else's power – is the instrument of toddler insurrection, along with tantrums, defiance and general negativity.

Just as language is beginning to develop, and with it the raw shards of self-consciousness and identity, so arrives the overwhelming need to take control of one's life. Grazyna Kochanska and colleagues from the University of Iowa wanted to see how the way parents exercised power over their very young children shaped their development.[4] Taking 101 two-parent families with a young child, they observed how the parents responded to their child at age two to three years, both when the children had been asked to tidy away some toys that the researchers provided, and when the children were told not to touch some very attractive toys which were placed temptingly on a shelf. It's remarkable how quickly people forget that they are being observed after some time, particularly in their own home. And so the parents' responses to the children flowed quite naturally in spite of the female observer sitting quietly in the corner making systematic observations.

Every thirty seconds she rated how the parents exercised control over their children and rated each segment as to whether each parent ignored the child (a score of minus 2 on the power scale), made some sociable interaction without control (minus 1), gave gentle guidance such as suggesting or hinting (plus 1), assertive control such as direct commands 'no!' (plus 2), forceful control such involving anger, raised voice or threats (plus 3). There were also more forceful exertions of power, including assertive physical control like taking the toys from the child's hand (plus 4) and forceful physical control such as roughly taking the toy or giving a light slap (plus 5).

The parents of these two- to three-year-old children were given a 'power assertion' score relating to their interactions with them, based on these observations. The researchers then withdrew, but came back when the children were about four years old, and then again when they were around five and a half.

By the time they were four, the children whose parents had gained high scores on the power assertion observations two years earlier were more resentful and oppositional than those whose parents who had been more cautious in wielding their power. And at five and half years old, the children who had been subject to strong parental power assertion were much more disruptive and antisocial in their behaviour towards other children and adults. This was particularly true for children who did not have a secure emotional relationship with their parents, particularly their mothers.

It shouldn't be surprising that, if power is wielded over you in a heavy-handed way when you are a young child, you should in turn try to impose your will on other children in a similarly dominant way. Antisocial and disruptive behaviour ends up filling prisons and causing misery to billions of people. Research consistently shows that parents over-exerting the huge power they hold over children through harsh discipline and coercion is a major cause of such behaviour.

And, of course, if this is how you have learned to get control as a child, you will likely bring this pattern of behaviour into your adult relationships – exercising assertive power over your partner and children physically and mentally. Men brought up in this way, with their greater physical strength, may be more prone to physical power assertion, while women with this upbringing may be more prone to mental abuse of their partners. But both risk satisfying their thwarted need for power by abusing their children both physically and mentally – thus perpetuating a cultural cycle of self-defeating violence and psychological pathology.

Parents who exert their parental power in this way may feel like winners in the parent–child power struggle, but this is an example of the sort of winning which has a sting in the tail.

On 12 September 2007 a political event happened which sent shock waves across the globe. A stunned silence hung over the motionless crowd who had heard the announcement. Then one man leapt to his feet and the others followed, bawling out demands for explanation – 'Why?' 'Why now?' 'What's the reason?' The man at the helm of the world's third-largest economy, pale and visibly distressed, parried their questions, as if exhausted by the announcement he had just made in a faltering voice – that he was resigning forthwith as prime minister of Japan after just one year in office. The power of the political trauma he had just triggered was magnified by its unexpectedness.

Prime Minister Shinzo Abe had had a tough year. In the summer his party had – for the first time in its history – lost control of the upper house of parliament. He had promised the United States to continue to give Japanese military support in the Afghanistan war, but now there was the risk of severe loss of face if the political opposition vetoed their continued deployment. Shinzo Abe had experienced the sorts of enormous stresses that almost inevitably accompany enormous power.

As the chaotic press conference ended, Mr Abe was rushed to hospital suffering from 'severe exhaustion'. His chief cabinet secretary, Kaoru Yosano, explained the lead-up to the resignation, saying, 'Prime Minister Abe was going forward while examining whether his health could handle the severe schedule and heavy psychological pressure of being prime minister.'⁵ Abe himself blamed crippling diarrhoea which was later attributed to 'stress and fatigue'. He had been taking medication because of sleep difficulties and this accumulation of stress-related problems led to his being put on a saline drip following his admission to hospital.

Power makes us smarter, focused and unempathic for a reason: if it didn't, then no leader could function properly, because of the huge stress leaders come under. If they are guiding the fate of hundreds, thousands or millions of people, they simply cannot afford to put themselves in the shoes of individuals most of the time. Otherwise they would be paralysed, because the big policy decisions leaders have to make inevitably hurt some people while helping others.

You have to be tough to hold power and Shinzo Abe just wasn't tough enough. Take a look at the photographs of presidents or prime ministers over their first few years of power and see how quickly the stress ages them. To survive the demands of holding power you have to *want* power and you have to *enjoy* using it: power is about having an impact on people, and what politician, business leader, doctor, scientist, nurse, teacher or police officer doesn't say they want to have an impact on people for the better? The last thing we want is leaders who don't want to win power – we *need winners*. But we need winners who want to win for 'we' as much as for 'me'. We need people who are not, like Karen and the power-asserting parents of the young children, deluded into feeling that their exercise of power within their small circle is a meaningful form of winning. In short, we need winners who are fired up as much by a need for s power as by a need for p power.

*   *   *

In the year 1215 something quite unprecedented happened in a small island off the north-west coast of Eurasia. A document called Magna Carta was signed which, for the first time, limited the power of an absolute monarch, forbidding that any of his 'freemen' citizens could be punished except through the law of the land. This document was forced on an unwilling King John of England by a group of feudal barons and remains codified in the law of England to this day.

We saw in Chapter 1 how considerable power drives many people to believe that their achievements are god-given, and some to believe that they might be gods themselves. At a time when the English royalty believed its power to be the 'Divine Right of Kings', we can imagine how hard it was for John to swallow this inhibition of his heaven-sent powers.

In June 2003 President George W. Bush told Palestinian Prime Minister Abu Mazen[6] that God had told him to invade Iraq. Osama bin Laden also believed his actions to be divinely inspired. Such beliefs may be in part a symptom of intensely power-needy people's brains being distorted by power.

Constitutionally, George W. Bush had to cease being president after his second term. But the dictators of this world serve out their bloody reigns at their discretion, sorting out any inconvenient checks and balances with imprisonment, torture and murder. As do the international crime barons whose wielding of power brings countries such as Mexico to their knees. The International Criminal Court may be seen as a new Magna Carta of sorts and the national and international legal and political systems offer the best possibility of extending the democratic world's system of checks and balances to those vast areas of the world where people are victims of leaders deranged by overdoses of power. But the question remains: given that we must have leaders who have power, is there anything we can do to protect them – and ourselves, because they control so much of our lives – from the brain damage and mental disturbance of a power overdose?

One study in 1963 analysed the background of thirty politicians who had used their power corruptly and it concluded that severe early deprivation was associated with the corrupt use of power. Where such early deprivation was emotional, the power tended to be used for a compensatory self-aggrandisement. Purely material deprivation, on the other hand, tended to lead the politicians to seek power for material advantages – as if they were trying to forestall the sort of physical deprivation that had haunted their early years.[7]

But power can be attractive to the lonely ego which has not been given the immortality conferred by an Oscar. The power to control others can give an enormous satisfaction if it is s power-oriented, but can leave the power holder feeling spent and empty if it is pure p-power, ego-driven striving, as David Kipnis showed.

Nathanael Fast and colleagues from the University of Southern California discovered that some bosses who have a lot of power over their underlings behave decently, while others abuse their power by behaving aggressively.[8] But how can we tell whether a colleague will turn into a bully if given power?

Power, it seems, brings out the bully in a person – but only in some people. Who are they? Nathanael Fast discovered the answer – and what he discovered will send a shiver of appalled recognition down the spine of all who have worked in an organisation. Power makes bullies of people who feel inadequate in the role of boss. It is an awful implication of the famous Peter Principle: 'in a hierarchy every employee tends to rise to his level of incompetence'.[9] With power comes the demand to perform under the close and critical scrutiny of underlings, peers and bosses. Such power energises and smartens some people, but it stresses out others who might have functioned well in a less powerful position – as, for instance, Prime Minister Shinzo Abe might have.

Just as winning an Oscar acts as a safety signal for the ego, giving it a life-lengthening boost, so people who lack the confidence or competence in a powerful position feel their ego is under the threat of public humiliation and failure. If physically threatened by someone, a natural response is to react aggressively in defence. And it is no different if the ego is psychologically threatened by the public exposure of incompetence – it is a common and natural response to react aggressively in defence of the ego.

And who is it easiest to vent this aggression on? The underlings, of course, who lack the power to strike back. Incompetent bosses with low power also feel their egos under threat, and they may still have the inclination to strike out in defence, but their relative lack of power makes it difficult for them to do that. Bad bosses cause misery, death and destruction costing trillions of dollars worldwide. From office supervisors to national presidents, power corrupts too many and ennobles too few. Having power is stressful and in poorly structured corporations, organisations and states it is difficult for any boss not to feel inadequate. Poor organisation – chaotic nation states with competing factions vying for power, fast-growing companies with a driven founder, sclerotic state offices with under-motivated staff – virtually guarantees that the boss will come eventually to feel incompetent and inadequate.

This massive threat to their egos in these driven men – men seek these positions of power more readily and more often than women – leads to aggression against their underlings. In the case of dictators like Robert Mugabe, this aggression can be fatal for tens of thousands of people and cause millions to starve. Cognitive dissonance inevitably kicks into play in their brains' dACC and then the brain tries to balance out the inconsistency by generating the contempt for their underlings of the type that Karen had for Chris. If power's effect on the brain is such a huge brake on development, if it is such a drag on humans winning their main race – for survival – then we have to do something about it very urgently. In the last section of this chapter I make some suggestions that have emerged from this journey through the brain's corridors of power.

Power audit

Many of us know approximately what our body-mass index is, what our cholesterol levels are and what our blood pressure is. We might have a rough idea about our level of aerobic fitness. Ours are the first generations to have this intense body and health awareness and it is one reason why we are likely to live much longer than our parents and grandparents.

But do we know what our relationship with power is? Do we know the extent to which we are exercising power in our work and relationships? If we are teachers, managers, social workers, doctors, psychologists, civil servants, police officers, prison guards, bankers, financial traders, estate agents, sales people, or belong to any other profession or trade, are we aware of how we exercise any power we have and how it affects us? Similarly, are we aware of other people's power over us? These are important questions.

Everyone who has any power should ask themselves from time to time: 'Is power going to my head?' Ambition is a great thing but ask a friend or partner about your pattern of behaviour. What do they think your power motivations are? This is a deep-seated part of our personality that we are mostly unaware of, and so we usually have to ask other people who live and work with us if we want to get an accurate picture.

Auditing our need for power should include asking ourselves whether our ego-driven p power is counterbalanced by high levels of altruistic s power. If our need for power is mostly ego driven, then it could make us unhappy – we are much more at risk of becoming addicted to power and ultimately corrupted by it. It will also make it more likely that our closest relationships will break up and will leave us vulnerable to a number of personal problems, including alcohol and substance abuse. And if we feel inadequate to the demands of our powerful position, we run the risk of displaying aggression and even bullying behaviour towards our underlings.

People who have any control over the appointment of leaders – and everyone in a democracy does – need to pay much more attention to the potential leader's power psychology. Yes, we need leaders who want and can handle power, but we want them balanced in s power and p power, and we also need lots of 'don'ts' and 'nots' in their conscious and unconscious minds. We need detailed power audits of not only political leaders, but also potential bosses before they get control over other people.

One signal to be aware of is a large number of 'I's in their speech. As we have seen, power increases egocentricity and weakens empathy for others; it boosts self-confidence and can slacken your conscience by inclining you feel that the rules that apply to others do not extend to you. Another warning signal in a leader is where their need for power is above average for their rank and status, and in particular where their 'I'-ego-oriented p power appears to exceed their 'we'-social-oriented s power.

Fortunately, the methods exist to do this – analysing the spontaneous speech and writing of leaders in the systematic ways that I described earlier in the book allows us to get rough and ready assessments of their innermost needs for power. Power is the central ingredient of human relationships, Bertrand Russell pointed out, and while we talk about it a lot – who has it and who doesn't – we *don't* talk much about how much people are made sick by it – either by too much or by too little. Power should become as familiar a currency of thought and discussion and self-awareness as physical fitness and health are now. That is the challenge for this stage in humanity's psychological development.

And of course we must consider power in our personal relationships, particularly with our children. Children like and need limits and control – laissez-faire child rearing can be a source of distress, lack of confidence and uncertainty for a child. But this enormous power to control that parents have over their children can corrupt some mothers and fathers and lead to children whose lives are ruined by a sense of thwarted control and angry resentment at their powerless childhood. Parents and partners need to audit their own power in relationships and ask themselves whether they are overdosing on it.

Everyone who has power should also audit themselves for the distortions of thinking that power causes. Negotiating from a position of high power may help drive a hard bargain, but beware of the powerful negotiator who overplays his hand and causes the negotiations to collapse because of power-induced hubris.

And consider for a moment how many projects there are where a delivery time is estimated which is then overshot again and again. Mario Weick and Ana Guinote of the University of Canterbury in England showed that power makes people over-optimistic about the time it will take to achieve a goal.[10] This is because power focuses your attention on goals and when people pay close attention to something, it seems closer. So while power can strengthen people mentally, it can also lead to problems which can potentially be avoided if people audit their own power ego-involvement.

Democracy and human capital

The word *democracy* derives from the Greek word *demos,* meaning people, and *kratia,* meaning rule or power. Democracy was an ingenious invention of the citizens of classical Greece to distribute that most precious and potent of human resources – power – more evenly, at least among those citizens who were not slaves or women.

When free elections are held in a country previously under dictatorship, it is both heart-rending and inspiring to see long lines of impoverished people waiting from pre-dawn until dusk, usually in scorching heat, for the chance to gain that shred of power that a free vote confers. Democracy, education and wealth go hand in hand, and *empowerment* may be a key ingredient of their interrelationship.

Education physically builds brains and increases the intelligence of a population, as I showed in my book *Mind Sculpture,*[11] and education confers dramatically better health and longer lives. Why should this be? Education enrols a person into the network of human culture, into the accumulated history of ideas – such as democracy, freedom, power, responsibility, accountability, corruption and so on. Abstract ideas like these are enormously empowering, as are the associated practical skills for negotiating everyday life like arithmetic, reading and writing. If there is any doubt the power that ideas can have, witness how Karl Marx's dense, obscure text *Das Kapital*, written over many years in the British Library in London, changed the world for a century and dramatically shaped the lives of billions of people, killing tens of millions along the way. If that is not power, what is?

Educated people live longer and better, I suggest, partly because they are empowered by the empire of ideas into which education enrols them. That empowerment in turn physically shapes their brains in the ways I have described in this book: it makes them smarter, it makes them take initiative, it focuses their minds on goals, it makes them happier and more confident. Power also makes people inclined to think in more abstract ways. In Chapter 3 we saw how Pamela Smith of Radboud University and colleagues found that power makes you mentally sharper. This team also showed that just thinking about a time when you had a little power over someone makes you more likely to think in more abstract, and even more creative, ways.[12] The converse is also probably true – being able to think in abstract ways because of the way education extends mental horizons, makes people feel more powerful.

The people's revolutions of North Africa and the Middle East which started in early 2011 are strong evidence for this link between empowerment through education and the hunger for *kratia* for the *demos*. These well-educated young people, hungry for the ideas that they are now connected to through educa-tion and the Internet, felt empowered to try to overthrow the suffocating power of dictators and their unaccountable cabinets, most of whom were rendered mentally sick and incapable by the brain damage caused by excessive power.

*   *   *

Democratic governments are not the only source of power across the world – far from it. The 2008 financial crash that impoverished hundreds of millions of people across the world was caused by the toxic *winner effect* on bankers and traders whose brains were addled by the testosterone-fuelled 'success' of escalating profits which skewed their judgement and crushed any moral compass they may once have had.

Money is power and so extreme wealth risks causing the sort of brain damage that unfettered power can cause. People whose lives centre on money become unhappy and this unhappiness triggers attempts to combat the unhappiness by seeking even more money, Tim Kasser and his colleagues have shown.[13]

A friend who worked as a trader in the City of London told me that the huge annual bonuses caused these young men and women to be totally focused on money and the size of that bonus – it seemed to him that they seldom talked or thought about anything else. But money acts like a drug, Stephen Lea and Paul Webley of the University of Exeter in England have shown,[14] and the way drug addiction destroys judgement, degrades morality and makes people miserable is well documented. Too great a focus on money may have comparable effects.

The winning crowd

Timothy Gowers is a mathematician at Cambridge University and he teamed up with Terence Tao of the University of California for a project called Polymath, which was an attempt to democratise that most elitist of activities, mathematical discovery.[15] These two winners of the mathematical equivalent of the Nobel Prize, the Field Medal, showed that by opening up on an

Internet forum a number of mathematical problems to people of all mathematical abilities, they created a sort of mathematical 'super-brain', which researchers at Carnegie Mellon University showed resulted in quicker and better solutions to these tough mathematical problems.

This international super-brain ranged from Nobel-level scientists like Gowers and Tao who made frequent contributions to the forum, to more mathematically lowly individuals such as Jason Dyer, a high-school mathematics teacher in Arizona, who, while not being able to follow all the high-level mathematical arguments, still managed to make a significant contribution to one of the problems.

This is a vivid demonstration of the fact that a 'we' orientation and a 'democratic' distribution of power and status can connect up brains into super-computer-like grids which have a real chance of solving some of humanity's most pressing problems. A single human brain is the most complex entity in the known universe: six billion of these wired together could potentially achieve a transformation of human life.

And the same is true for organisations and corporations which want to compete and survive by creativity and nimbleness: if they can harness and connect up the combined computational capacities of their employees into a super-brain grid, then they should be able to thrive. But that requires empowerment, and an appreciation of all the obstacles that prevent individuals from winning – the sorts of obstacles that I described in Chapters 1, 2 and 3. The critical conclusion of this book is that what you are is a product of context in your home, social and working life.

Context has bigger effects earlier in life and, because of the young brain's greater malleability, some of that context can become burned into the synapses of the developing brain. But just as there is a curse of genetic fatalism that can sabotage our achievements in a self-fulfilling-prophecy manner, so there is a parallel curse of 'early childhood fatalism' which can disable people in a similar manner by leading them to assume that these early experiences are indelible. In extreme cases they may be, but the crucial thing to understand is that the human brain is malleable *throughout life*, as I showed in *Mind Sculpture*.

A key part of 'context' is the role you are given. Many people, for instance, 'rise to the challenge' when promoted to a position of responsibility, and, like the African cichlid fish, will change physically and mentally as a result. Some of your colleagues or employees, or your family, may have huge potential which is not realised because they have not been given the chance.

One of the greatest haemorrhages of the world super-brain arises from the disempowerment of older people whose memories are needlessly worsened by negative stereotypes, as we saw in Chapter 2. Except in dictators or media magnates, age usually brings with it a softening of the ego's drive for power and attention. P-power motivation among older people may decline as testosterone levels fall, but the s-power motivation may rise in compensation. Big egos are a huge problem for connected super-brains because they disrupt the democracy of information flow. Older people could be empowered by connecting them to the super-brain, and in giving them this power, we will also make them individually smarter, by giving their testosterone and dopamine levels a brain-nourishing boost.

Power of the group

Being in a majority confers power on its members, and can lead the majority to have contempt for the minority, just as Karen developed contempt for Chris. This can, of course, lead to the majority treating the minority badly and, once they do this, their dACC dissonance-reducing brain circuits justify their behaviour by magnifying the contempt and sharpening a derogatory attitude to the minority.

But you don't have to be in a majority for this sort of neuropsychological dynamic to happen. It is easier to mobilise millions of people if they have the feeling of power that comes from being in the majority – as Hitler did with the Germans and Austrians – but you need more than this for a mass pogrom. Power holders who feel inadequate become aggressive bullies more easily, and the egos of the German population in the 1920s were bruised by the humiliating terms of the post-Great War settlement imposed on them by France and the allies. This once powerful industrial giant of Europe was further humiliated and made to feel inadequate by poverty and starvation.

The German people's tender egos and power-sapped brains were therefore hungry and needy of any power that could come their way – and the meagre power of being the majority over the Jewish minority was a tiny flame that Hitler carefully nurtured into a fire. He did this in many ways, but a key one was the classic technique of the bully – he tricked hitherto millions of largely neutral people into taking some small negative action against the victims, which then set off the vicious spiral of cognitive dissonance, where the dACC rationalises the bully's actions so that he concludes that the victims must be really bad people – 'Otherwise why is a good person like me doing this to them?'

Hitler did this by passing laws which made ordinary German citizens – shopkeepers, civil servants, police and so on – create some initially small inconvenience against Jewish people. Once they took this action, the mass manipulation of tens of millions of brains began, which rationalised what they were doing to their Jewish neighbours and customers, leading them to conclude that the Jews must be in some way bad and deserving of their fate. Once this process had begun, Hitler used further laws to make them act in more and more negative ways towards the Jews, and so on until the apocalyptic conclusion. This was again a perverted form of 'winning' which sowed the seeds of its own destruction.

Similar dynamics have played out in Bosnia, Rwanda, Darfur and other places. But these are not inevitable symptoms of the evil lurking in all human beings through our genetically endowed and irresistible biological primitive urges. If governments have the will to do so, they can implement policies that will shape the behaviour of their citizens towards out-groups, and such changes may reshape the brains of millions of people, via the dACC and cognitive dissonance, to create more positive feelings towards the stigmatised groups. And if governments can contrive situations and policies where the prejudiced group find themselves doing small *positive* things for the victimised, then cognitive dissonance will cause them to think, 'If I am doing this for them then they must be nice people.'

What makes a winner?

'I' is a lonely animal which even winning an Oscar cannot make immortal. The vulnerability of the corrupted leader's ego lies behind the poverty, starvation and butchery of millions. A single ego-focused boss can make life a misery. This intense drive to *win* that most of us feel from time to time is part of nothing less than a life-or-death struggle for 'I'.

Yet 'I' doesn't really exist outside a network of relationships with other people. So when we engage in a struggle for 'I' to *win,* it is a race that can never be won, because 'I' is a bit of a chimera. This is why people with an intense ego-driven need for p power acquire a continually growing appetite for power that can never be satisfied. Only where there is a strong s-power need to balance the p power, do we see a healthy psychological relationship with power and an escape from its drug-addiction properties. This is winning without a sting in the tail.

But the genie 'I' is out the bottle and the individualistic culture of the West has spurred brilliant individuals to great scientific achievements, producing proportionally many more Nobel Prizes than in Eastern cultures, where 'I' is a more social beast embedded in a more collective identity.[16] In Chapter 2 we saw that the lonely 'I' can often only deal with power's effects by attributing their personal power to god-given gifts – or, in some bad cases of the 'illness', – to being a god himself. Religion is not necessarily a bulwark against hubris and its effects and can sometimes act as an amplifier of power intoxication. But most religions and ethical systems do have strictures that attempt to limit the self-aggrandisement of the power-intoxicated winner.

What makes a *real* winner then – as opposed to a Karen or a Robert Mugabe, whose distorted brains believe themselves to have won? Real winners enjoy the benefits of power – the testosterone-fuelled drive, smartness, creativity and goal-focus – and enjoy influencing other people by dispensing resources that other people need and want. They thrive on being able to have an *impact* and they do not cripple themselves by believing their success to be due to inherited, unchangeable qualities – intuitively winners know that the greatest obstacle to success can be self-handicapping beliefs such as 'I can't do that because I'm not *bright, outgoing, ambitious, tough* [add any other adjectives you care to] enough.'

Winners are to a considerable extent made by their circum-stances and environments – most of us can become winners by rising to a challenge and we can *get better* if we are put into a position of power and influence. But sometimes we don't benefit from such circumstances because of unconscious prejudices and stereotypes in our own and others' brains. Leaders must have an appetite for power – the stress will be too great if they don't – but the hunger has to be as much for power for the benefit of others – s power – as for sustenance for the ego – p power. Power-hungry national leaders go to war more often, so we must carefully judge what sort of power need they have: true winners seek power as much for the social *s* as they do for the ego *p*.

Winners feel in control of life, and that sense of control will help shield them from stress and help them succeed better and live longer and happier. But true winners appreciate that, no matter how much of chimera it is, the ego is a dangerous dog. The men and women who take on the burden of power and use it well always keep the dog at a certain distance and on a tight leash of accountability to principles beyond themselves. Taming 'I' may be the greatest challenge for mankind's success.

Afterword

Many writers succumb to the delusion that their books speak to the future of the world. Let me indulge myself in such a conceit: the world is suffering very serious environmental, social and military challenges. January 2011 showed that it is no longer possible to contain a situation where young men and women connected electronically to the wider world will tolerate extremes of political and economic inequality. With a burgeoning population exceeding the water, food and energy capacities of the world, a growing and spreading arsenal of weapons of mass destruction, and a threatened climatic meltdown, the human race has to take some very serious actions.

And perhaps the greatest obstacle to facing up to these questions is the difficulty of curbing the toxic effects of power on the brains of the people who will make decisions and policies to deal with the challenges. The minority of countries in the world which are democracies have developed a sophisticated set of mechanisms – elections, independent judiciaries, a free press and so on – of accountability, whose principal function is to prevent power holders becoming addicted to power and as a consequence neurologically deranged by it.

The world is slowly coming together to recognise and deal with global warming – perhaps too late – but still there is a huge move towards non-fossil energies, carbon capture, carbon trading and the like. What we need now is a similar, international effort to recognise and deal with the effects of power on the human brain.

Winning can be quite easy if we learn the tricks of manipulating other people. The human brain has similarities to a big multinational corporation whose left hand often doesn't know what the right hand is doing and people can gain power over others by tricks which capitalise on this size and complexity. Dominating your family can also be easy – you can apply more or less crude behavioural control methods, from physical threat and punishment to threat of abandonment and emotional blackmail. At home you can become a 'winner' in the inevitable family battles for control.

At work the cute operator who is tuned to hierarchies can climb the greasy pole by using influence tricks, as well as old familiar methods like ingratiation, undermining competitors and bullying underlings. If the cute operator's bosses are power-needy individuals driven by p-rather than s-power motivation, they will in their egotism tend to be blind to the machinations of those below them and will take flattery at face value – as due homage to their greatness, in other words. And so they will succumb to the tricks and advance the ascent of their ambitious underlings.

The nurse responsible for the care of vulnerable people may, if their clients are unlucky, enjoy wielding the near-total power they have over these people's lives. In their small princedom they will be an all-powerful winner. We know well now what the effects of power on the brain are and power given to the wrong person will make them see their clients as objects, not people.

Their behaviour towards them will deteriorate and the consist-ency-seeking parts of their brains will rationalise this behaviour in their brains to make them develop a contempt and loathing for their clients.

The teacher who has the power to make or break careers by the grades they award and the instruction they offer may succeed in dominating generations of students, and the doctor, surgeon or psychologist who becomes too fond of the power they hold over their patients may come to abuse it. The police officer who has the power to arrest you and the prison officer who keeps you locked up in your cell are in positions of power where we are most familiar with the dangers of abuse. When these uniformed officers have a malign need to win for the wrong reasons, they can have their brains scrambled by the power they hold.

Karen was a winner in her battle with Chris, but it made her unhappy. David Kipnis and his colleagues,[1] found that when they showed volunteers how to manipulate other people using the various influence techniques such as the mental foot in the door of my asthma salesman, it made the volunteers feel less good about themselves. This chimes with what happens to those who make the search for that other major source of power – money – central to their lives: the more focused a person is on money and materialism, the less happy they tend to feel.[2] Power is like a drug, after all, and we know that while drugs can make us feel good in the short run, in the long term they can make us feel miserable. So should we be trying to eradicate this terrible drug? Is power a dangerous source of evil in the world?

Of course it is. But it is also a huge source of good – and we call that good, leadership. Without the leadership of Winston Churchill and Franklin D. Roosevelt, for instance, I would likely be a loyal fascist citizen of the Greater German Empire and my children would be uniformed members of the Hitler

Youth. Martin Luther King had the power to call out millions of supporters on to the streets and President Lula da Silva of Brazil helped make his country one of the world's leading economies: they were leaders with power who used it for the benefit of countless people.

So what do we do about this drug that is both so wonderful and so destructive? How do we create winners who win proper victories that benefit us all rather than mere short-sighted triumphs that benefit nothing except their egos? How do we prevent the Mugabes of this world from an insatiable craving for power that starves a nation and murders its citizens? How do we prevent the power- and greed-intoxicated Wall Street managers of this world cynically playing the markets by selling precarious stock to innocent customers while simultaneously short-selling the very same stock on the markets and hence precipitating its collapse?

The puzzle of Enron offered an apparent solution to this problem – the possibility that giving more power to more women might lead to less corruption. As we saw in Chapter 5, women have, on average, higher levels of s-power motivation than men. Are women then safer bets on whom to bestow power?

They may be, although Shira Keshet and colleagues at Bar-Ilan University in Israel found that women when given power start to behave more like men in the way they use it.[3] Female world leaders such as Margaret Thatcher, Falklands War leader and former Prime Minister of Britain, illustrate this point, as does former Israeli Prime Minister Golda Meir, the first 'Iron Lady' of international politics. Even long before the twentieth century, Catherine the Great of Russia and Queen Elizabeth I of England wielded considerable power, while the Empress Irene, ruler of the Byzantine Empire in the eighth century, insisted that only eunuchs could be members of her governing cabinet and had her own son blinded for rebellion.[4]

The behaviour of concentration-camp guards in Nazi Germany, in Cambodia, in Stalin's gulags, in Serbian Bosnia and in scores of other places is not a manifestation of some inevitable biological drive towards cruelty bred into the human brain. Rather it is what happens when individual camp commandants and guards are given complete power over others without legal and bureaucratic restraints and in the absence of a leadership demanding standards of decency. Once these figures receive such unfettered power, almost inevitably they start to see their inmates as things, not people, and the rationalising circuits in their brains amplify their contempt and hatred for them in order to justify their cruelty. Their brains scrambled by power, they lose perspective and their behaviour descends to levels that would be unthinkable to them in another setting or time. They are cichlid fish – albeit with the human being's limited capacity for insight and self-reflection – changed utterly by this new environment.

Unthinkable cruelty on a mass scale can be turned on and off like an electric switch. The Rwandan massacres of 1994 were planned and orchestrated by a small number of political leaders who gave the orders for the genocide over the radio, and tens of thousands of willing Hutu listeners butchered hundreds of thousands of their Tutsi neighbours. There was preparation via hate propaganda trickling out over the previous months, but the Hutus who hacked the Tutsis to death were not genetically programmed to do this. They were in fact programmed by the influence technologies deployed by political leaders for political reasons – and the technologies were not much more sophisticated than those the asthma salesman used on me that sunny morning in Cambridge.

Unlike the cichlid fish, the human being can be changed fundamentally by ideas as well as by a changed environment. This can make the owners of the mass media as powerful as politicians – Silvio Berlusconi held power in Italy partly because of his grip on both media and government. Rupert Murdoch, head of News International, could make or break governments by telling his tabloids to support or oppose a party: Tony Blair famously took time to fly to Australia in the middle of a frantic election campaign in 1997 just to secure Murdoch's support for New Labour in Britain.

Democratic politicians have many checks on their appetite for power – that is what democracy is all about. But media press barons have no such checks on the enormous power they wield – no elections, no civil servants, little critical press, scarce legal restraint and no financial accountability except to shareholders. Such unfettered, unchecked power disrupts the brains of many of those who hold it – and eventually may corrupt them. Non-democratic politicians have their brains even more scrambled by the total power they wield – at least press barons do not have armies, prisons, police and national treasuries with which to exercise power. Dictators are made mentally sick by the overdose of power which overwhelms their brain chemistry. The consequences of this for hundreds of millions of people are truly dreadful. That is why power's effects on the human brain constitute a challenge as great as global warming.

'What we need is a benevolent dictator.' How often have we heard this said about an organisation or government? But unfortunately, as we have seen throughout this book, there can be no such thing as a benevolent dictator – unfettered power at any level will damage the normal functioning of a dictator's brain and lead to corruption and abuse of power. Good governance from the highest level of the state down to the hospital clinic, the boardroom, the classroom, the factory and the office is the main bulwark against the susceptibility of the human brain to the damaging effects of power.

Leaders must have power, but they have to feel constrained
and accountable in their use of it – to some degree held in check
by other people and systems. For example, police in most democratic countries must make audio recordings of their interviews
with suspects: their power over people in custody has to be
constrained by this scrutiny. Doctors and surgeons also need to
be monitored by their peers and bosses to make sure that their
power over patients is not going to their heads. Everyone who
has power over other people should have some accountability
for the way they exercise that power – this is what good governance is.

The International Criminal Court is an enormous step forward
in the human race's attempt to address the problems caused by
power's corrupting effects on the brain. The referral of the dictator Muammar Gaddafi to the ICC in February 2011, the arrest
warrant issued for the Sudanese President Omar al-Bashir for
war crimes in Darfur, and many similar cases, are examples of
the most significant attempt to deal with the problem of power
and the human brain since the development of democracy.

Such measures are necessary because leaders with too much
unfettered power will never be able to have the sort of insight
that would lead them to recognise their troubled behaviour –
just as drug addicts at first, or in some cases for ever, lack insight
into the terrible mess their lives have become.

But as every addiction counsellor knows, there can be no
change without naming the problem. Putting words to it is the
starting point of gaining insight into its grip on you. This book's
aim is to help *name* the problem of power – not just in politics and high finance – but also at the manager's desk and the
family's kitchen table. The diagnosis of power-induced illness
– or vulnerability to developing the disease – in leaders, bosses,
partners and parents must become as common a currency of

discussion as the consideration of their physical health. Only if we all become aware of what power *is* and what it *does*, is there a chance of greater insight on the part of the real power holders. They need to know that the wrong kind of power makes you sick.

Notes

Prologue

1. http://www.forbes.com/lists/2008/18/biz_2000globalo8_
   The-Global-2000_Assets.html
2. *The Times*, London, 22 March 2009.
3. *The Times*, London, 20 January 2009.
4. *Daily Telegraph*, London, 1 February 2010.
5. *New York Daily News*, 13 February 2011.
6. *New York Times*, 25 February 2011.
7. http://www.forbes.com/wealth/power-women/list
8. *New York Times* 21 May 2009.
9. Jessica Shambora, CNN Money, 22 May 2009 http://postcards.blogs.
   fortune.cnn.com/2009/05/22/xeroxs-next-ceo-ursula-burns/

1: The Mystery of Picasso's Son

1. Marina Picasso, *Picasso: My Grandfather*, London, Chatto and Windus,
   2001, p.9.
2. Marina Picasso, *Picasso: My Grandfather*, London, Chatto and Windus,
   2001, p.11.
3. Gladwell, Malcolm, *Blink: The Power of Thinking Without Thinking*, New
   York, Little, Brown and Company, 2005, p.86.

4. Bennedsen, M., et al., *The Quarterly Journal of Economics*, 122 (2007), pp.647–691.
5. Luthar, S., and D'Avanzano, K., *Development and Psychopathology*, 11 (1999), pp.845–867; Buss, D.M., *American Psychologist*, 55 (2000), pp.15–23.
6. Way N., Stauber, H.Y., Nakkula, M.J., and London, P., 'Depression and substance use in two divergent high school cultures: A quantitative and qualitative analysis', *Journal of Youth and Adolescence*, 23 (1994), pp.331–357.
7. Luthar, S.S., and Becker, B.E., *Child Development*, 73 (2002), pp.1593–1610.
8. Linder, S., *The Harried Leisure Class*, New York, Columbia University Press, 1970.
9. *New York Times*, 28 April 1996, interview by Michael Kimmelman with Pablo Picasso's wife Françoise Gilot and his surviving children Claude, Paloma and Maya.
10. Helen Langdon, *Caravaggio: A Life*, London, Pimlico, 1999, p.382.
11. Andrew Graham-Dixon, *Caravaggio: A Life Sacred and Profane*, London: Allen Lane, 2010, p.420.
12. *The Times*, London, 12 November 1973.
13. *The Times*, London, 17 December 1973.
14. Getty, J.P., *As I See It: The Autobiography of J. Paul Getty*, Los Angeles, Getty Publications, 2003, p.335; see also: http://blogs.forbes.com/robertlenzner/2011/01/22/plutocracy-the-rich-elite-and-their-duty/
15. Interview with Maura Egan, *New York Times*, 23 September 2001.
16. Interview with Maura Egan, *New York Times*, 23 September 2001.
17. *New York Times*, 7 February 2011.
18. Ray, J.J., *Australian Psychologist*, 14 (1979), pp.337–344.
19. Mizuno, K., et al., *NeuroImage*, 42 (2008), pp.369–378.
20. Maehr, M.L., in Ames, R.E., and Ames, C., *Research on Motivation in Education*, New York, Academic Press, 1984, pp.115–144.
21. Fliessbach, K., et al., *Science*, 318 (2007), pp.1305–1308.
22. Miner, J.B., et al., *Journal of Applied Psychology*, 74 (1989), pp.554–560.
23. Ray, J.J., and Singh, S., *The Journal of Social Psychology*, 112 (1980), pp.11–17.
24. *Sunday Times*, London, 2 July 2006.
25. http://givingpledge.org/
26. McClelland, D.C., *The Achieving Society*, New York, Irvington Publishers, 1961, p.356.
27. O'Doherty, F., *Irish Medical News*, 27 September 2010, p.44.
28. Crandall, V.C., Katkovsky, W., and Crandall, V. J., *Child Development*, 36 (1965), pp.91–109.
29. Diener, C., and Dweck, C., *Journal of Personality and Social Psychology*, 36 (1978), pp.451–462.

30. Diener, C., and Dweck, C., *Journal of Personality and Social Psychology*, 39 (1980), pp.940–952.
31. Blackwell, L., et al., *Child Development*, 78 (2007), pp.246–263.
32. Covington, M., *Annual Review of Psychology*, 51 (2000), pp.171–200.
33. Mangels, J., et al., *Social Cognitive and Affective Neuroscience*, 1 (2006), pp.75–86.
34. Duckworth, A.L., *Journal of Personality and Social Psychology*, 92 (2007), pp.1087–1101.
35. Bennett, D.A., et al., *Lancet Neurology*, 5 (2006), pp.406–12.
36. Dweck, C.S., and Leggett, E.L., *Psychological Review*, 95 (1988), pp.256–273.
37. Ericsson, K.A., et al., *Psychological Review* 100 (1993), pp.363–406.

2: *The Puzzle of the Changeling Fish*

1. Cashdan, E., *Aggressive Behavior*, 29 (2003), pp.107–115.
2. Bernhardt, P.C., et al., *Physiology and Behavior*, 65 (1998), pp.59–62.
3. *Independent*, London, 25 September 1995.
4. William McIlvanney, *Sunday Times*, London, 24 December 1995.
5. Landau, H.G., *Bulletin of Mathematical Biophysics*, 13 (1951), pp.1–19.
6. Landau, H.G., *Bulletin of Mathematical Biophysics*, 13 (1951), pp. 245–262.
7. McDonald, N. W., Heimstra, A. L., and Damkot, D. K., 'Social modification of agonistic behaviour in fish', *Animal Behaviour*, 16 (1968), pp.437–441.
8. Mazur, Allan, Booth, Alan, and Dabbs, James M. Jr., 'Testosterone and Chess Competition', *Social Psychology Quarterly*, 55 (1992), pp.70–77.
9. Robins, L.N., Davis, D.H., and Nurco, D.N., 'How permanent was Vietnam drug addiction?', *American Journal of Public Health Supplement*, 64 (1974), pp.38–43.
10. Siegel, S., et al., *Science*, 216 (1982), pp.436–437.
11. Hill, R.A., and Barton, R.A., 'Red enhances human performance in contests: Signals biologically attributed to red colouration in males may operate in the arena of combat sports', *Nature*, 435 (2005), p.293.
12. Bellizzi, Joseph A., and Hite, Robert E., 'Environmental colour, consumer feelings, and purchase likelihood', *Psychology and Marketing*, 9 (1992), pp.347–363.
13. Pryke, S., 'Is red an innate or learned signal of aggression and intimidation?', *Animal Behaviour*, 78 (2009), pp.393–398.

14. Khan, S.A., et al., *Psychological Science*, 22 (2011), pp.1001–1003.
15. http://www.maltavista.net/en/list/photo/1527.html
16. Neave, Nick, and Wolfson, Sandy, 'Testosterone, territoriality, and the "home advantage", *Physiology and Behavior*, 78 (2003), pp.269–275.
17. Pollard, R., 'Worldwide regional variations in home advantage in association football', *Journal of Sports Sciences*, 24 (2006), pp.231–240.
18. Brown, Graham, and Baer, Markus, 'Location in negotiation: Is there a home field advantage?', *Organizational Behaviour and Human Decision Processes*, 2011, pp.114, 190–200.
19. Mayfield, J., Mayfield, M., Martin, D., and Herbig, P., 'How location impacts international business negotiations', *Review of Business*, 19 (1998), pp.21–24.
20. Schubert, Thomas W., and Koole, Sander L., 'The Embodied Self: Making a Fist Enhances Men's Power-related Self-conceptions', *Journal of Experimental Social Psychology*, 45 (2009), pp.828–834.
21. *Guardian*, London, 30 November 2010.
22. Carney, D.R., et al., *Psychological Science*, 21 (2010), p.1363.
23. http://money.cnn.com/magazines/fortune/fortune500/2009/womenceos/
24. Plant, E. Ashby, et al., 'The Obama Effect: Decreasing Implicit Prejudice and Stereotyping', *Journal of Experimental Social Psychology*, 45 (2009), pp.961–964.
25. Rudman, Laurie A. Greenwald, Anthony G., and McGhee, Debbie E., 'Implicit Self-Concept and Evaluative Implicit Gender Stereotypes: Self and Ingroup Share Desirable Traits', *Personality and Social Psychology Bulletin*, 27 (2001), pp.1164–1117.
26. Phelps, Elizabeth A., O'Connor, Kevin J., Cunningham, William A., Funayama, E. Sumie, Gatenby, J. Christopher, Gore, John. C., and Banji, Mahzarin R., 'Performance on indirect measures of race evaluation predicts amygdala activation', *Journal of Cognitive Neuroscience*, 12 (2000), pp.729–738.
27. *Miami Herald*, Wednesday, 12 August 2010.
28. *Journal of Personality and Social Psychology*, 2 (1965), pp.53–59.
29. Kiefer, A.K., and Sekaquaptewa, D., 'Implicit stereotypes and women's math performance: How implicit gender-math stereotypes influence women's susceptibility to stereotype threat', *Journal of Experimental Social Psychology*, 43 (2007), pp.825–832.
30. Bargh, J., et al., *Journal of Personality and Social Psychology*, 71 (1996), pp.230–244.
31. Hess, Thomas M., Hinson, Joey T., and Statham, Jill A., 'Explicit and Implicit Stereotype Activation Effects on Memory: Do Age and Awareness Moderate the Impact of Priming?', *Psychology and Aging*, 19 (2004), pp.495–505.

32. Hess, Thomas M., Auman, Corinne, Colcombe, Stanley J., and Rahhal, Tamara A. 'The Impact of Stereotype Threat on Age Differences in Memory Performance', *Journal of Gerontology: Psychological Sciences*, 58B (2003), pp.3–11.

3: *The Enigma of Bill Clinton's Friend*

1. Halberstam, D., *War in a Time of Peace: Bush, Clinton and the Generals*, London, Bloomsbury, 2002, p.423.
2. *New York Times*, 25 October 1993.
3. Mould, R.F., *Chernobyl Record: The Definitive History of the Chernobyl Catastrophe*, London, Taylor and Francis, 2000; *see also*: http://www.world-nuclear.org/info/chernobyl/info7.html
4. Rosen, S., and Tesser, A., *Sociometry*, 33 (1970), pp.253–263.
5. Hofstede, G., *Culture's Consequences*, 2nd edn. London, Sage, 2001, p.79.
6. Hofstede, G., *Culture's Consequences*, 2nd edn. London, Sage, 2001, p.502.
7. Hofstede, G., *Culture's Consequences*, 2nd edn. London, Sage, 2001, p.500.
8. Powell, J., *The New Machiavelli: How to Wield Power in the Modern World*, London, Bodley Head, 2010, pp.6, 60.
9. *Guardian*, London, 2 February 2010.
10. Clarke, A., *Barbarossa: The Russian-German Conflict 1941–45*, New York, William Morrow and Company, 1965.
11. Galinsky, A.D., et al., *Psychological Science*, 17 (2006), pp.1068–1074.
12. Fast, N.J., et al., *Psychological Science* 20 (2009), pp.502–508.
13. Hermann, M.G., in Post, J.M. (ed.), *The Psychological Assessment of Political Leaders*, Ann Arbor, University of Michigan Press, 2005, p.315.
14. Dyson, S.B., *Foreign Policy Analysis*, 2 (2006), pp.289–306.
15. Campbell, A., *The Blair Years: Extracts from the Alastair Campbell Diaries*, London, Random House, 2007, p.567.
16. Powell, Jonathon, *Great Hatred, Little Room: Making Peace in Northern Ireland*, London, The Bodley Head, 2008, p.10.
17. Woodward, Bob, *Washington Post*, Wednesday, 21 April 2004, p.A01; http://www.washingtonpost.com/wp-dyn/articles/A28710-2004Apr20.html
18. Smith, P.K., et al., *Psychological Science*, 19 (2008), pp.441–447.
19. Guinote, A., *Journal of Experimental Social Psychology*, 43 (2007), pp.685–697.
20. Mullins, C., Kirley, A., Gill, M., and Robertson, I.H, *Biological Psychiatry*, 60 (2006), pp.1039–1045; Greene, C.M., Bellgrove, M.A., Gill, M., and Robertson, I.H., *Neuropsychologia*, 47 (2009), pp.591–594.

21. Winter, D.G., *The Power Motive*, New York, Free Press, 1973.
22. Hermann, M.G., in Post, J.M. (ed.), *The Psychological Assessment of Political Leaders*, Ann Arbor, University of Michigan Press, 2005.
23. Wirth, M.M., et al., *Hormones and Behaviour*, 49 (2006), pp.346–352.
24. Schultheiss, O.C., et al., *Social Cognitive and Affective Neuroscience*, 3 (2008), pp.333–343.
25. Schultheiss, O.C., *Journal of Research in Personality*, 37 (2003), pp.224–230.
26. http://www.forbes.com/profile/dominique-strauss-kahn/
27. http://www.nytimes.com/2011/05/17/world/europe/17fund.html?_r=1
28. http://www.guardian.co.uk/world/2010/apr/29/vladimir-putin-polar-bear-arctic; http://www.guardian.co.uk/news/blog/2008/sep/01/russia
29. http://www.forbes.com/profile/angela-merkel/

4: The Mystery of the Oscars

1. Associated Press report by Bob Thomas, April 2008, archived in http://web.archive.org/web/20080409211126/http://ap.google.com/article/ALeqM5hIhnqF6LygGpQ54CQdntp6c74tTwD8VSHEV81
2. The original observation about the Oscars effect was made in Redelmeier, D.A., and Singh, S.M., *Annals of Internal Medicine*, 134 (2001), pp.955–962. The statistical method was criticised later in Sylvestre, M.P., et al., *Annals of Internal Medicine*, 145 (2006), pp.361–363, but these criticisms were successfully addressed in a further reanalysis by the original authors in Redelemeier, D.A., and Singh, S.M., *Annals of Internal Medicine*, 145 (2006), p.392.
3. Rablen, M.D., and Oswald, A.J., *Journal of Health Economics* 27 (2008), pp.1462–1471.
4. Smith, G.D., et al., *British Medical Journal*, 305 (1992), pp.1554–1557.
5. Rablen, M.D., and Oswald, A.J., *Journal of Health Economics* 27 (2008), pp.1462–1471.
6. Christopher Meyer, *DC Confidential*, Weidenfeld & Nicolson, London, 2005.
7. http://www.dtic.mil/cgi-bin/GetTRDoc?AD=ADA058122&Location=U2&doc=GetTRDoc.pdf
8. Sapolsky, R.M., *Science*, 308 (2005), pp.648–665.
9. Zink, C.F., et al., *Neuron*, 58 (2008), pp.273–283.
10. Sapolsky, R.M., *Science*, 308 (2005), pp.648–665.
11. Marmot, M.G., et al., *The Lancet*, 337 (1991), pp.1387–1393.

12. *The Times*, London, 30 May 2006.

13. Moore, L.T., et al., *American Journal of Human Genetics*, 78 (2006), pp.334–338.

14. Marmot, M.G., et al., *The Lancet*, 337 (1991), pp.1387–1393.

15. Seligman, M.E.P., *Annual Review of Medicine*, 23 (1972), pp.407–412.

16. http://www.dtic.mil/cgi-bin/GetTRDoc?Location=U2&doc=GetTRDoc.pdf&AD=ADA058122

17. Collins, B.E., *Journal of Personality and Social Psychology*, 29 (1974), pp.381–391.

18. Pruessner, J.C., et al., *NeuroImage*, 28 (2005), pp.815–826.

19. Baumeister, R.F., *Journal of Personality and Social Psychology*, 52 (1987), pp.163–176.

20. Han, S., et al., *Social Neuroscience*, 3 (2007), pp.1–15.

21. Dickerson, Sally S., and Kemeny, Margaret E., *Psychological Bulletin*, 130 (2004), pp.355–391.

22. Cole, S., et al., *Journal of Personality and Social Psychology*, 72 (1997), pp.320–336.

23. Dickerson, S., et al., *Journal of Personality*, 72 (2004), pp.1191–1216.

24. Levi, P., *If This Is a Man*, London, Penguin Modern Classics, 1979, p.85.

25. Pollak, D.D., et al., *Neuron*, 60 (2008), pp.149–161.

5: *The Riddle of the Flying CEOs*

1. http://abcnews.go.com/Blotter/WallStreet/story?id=6285739&page=1

2. http://www.msnbc.msn.com/id/28015687/ns/business-autos/t/gm-ceo-heading-capitol-way-malibu/

3. *New York Times*, 2 November 2008.

4. *BusinessWeek*, 15 May 2000; http://www.businessweek.com/2000/00_20/b3681075.htm

5. Enron Corporation Annual Report 2000; http://picker.uchicago.edu/Enron/EnronAnnualReport2000.pdf

6. Tippmann-Peikert, M., et al., *Neurology*, 68 (2007), pp.301–303.

7. Dodd, M. Leann, et al., *Archives of Neurology*, 62 (2005), pp.1377–1381.

8. Franken, I.H.A., *Progress in Neuro-Psychopharmacology and Biological Psychiatry*, 27 (2003), pp.563–579.

9. *New York Times*, 18 January 2011; *Daily Telegraph*, London, 22 March 2011.

10. Cited in Kets de Vries, M.F.R., *Leaders, Fools, and Impostors*, Lincoln, NE, iUniverse, 1993, p.31.

11. Bellgrove, M.A., Chambers, C.D., Johnson, K.A., Daibhis, A., Daly, M., Hawi. Z., Lambert, D., Gill, M., and Robertson, I.H., *Molecular Psychiatry*, 12 (2007), pp.786–792.

12. Bellgrove, M.A., Hawi, Z., Lowe, N., Kirley, A., Robertson, I.H., and Gill, M., *American Journal of Medical Genetics Part B: Neuropsychiatric* 136B (2005), pp.81–86.

13.Dreber, Anna, Rand, David G., Wernerfelt, Nils, Garcia, Justin R., Lum, J. Koji, and Zeckhauser, Richard, 'Dopamine and Risk Choices in Different Domains: Findings Among Serious Tournament Bridge Players', Harvard Kennedy School Faculty Research Working Paper Series RWP10-034, July 2010.

14. Garavan, H., et al., *American Journal of Psychiatry*, 157 (2000), pp.1789–1798.

15. Nestler, E.J., *Nature Neuroscience*, 8 (2005), pp.1445–1449.

16. Schultheiss, Oliver C., Dargel, Anja, and Rohde, Wolfgang, *Journal of Research in Personality*, 37 (2003), pp.224–230.

17. Lammers, J., et al., *Psychological Science*, 22 (2011), pp.1191–1197.

18. Bargh, J. A., Raymond, P., Pryor, J. B., and Strack, F., *Journal of Personality and Social Psychology*, 68 (1995), pp.768–781.

19. *Houston Chronicle*, 15 February 2004.

20. For a number of such examples see: Jackson, R., and Beilock, S.L., 'Attention and performance', in Farrow, D., Baker, J., and MacMahon, C. (eds.), *Developing Elite Sports Performers: Lessons from Theory and Practice*, Routledge, New York, 2008, pp.104–118.

21. Mobbs, D., et al., *Psychological Science*, 20 (2009), pp.955–962.

22. http://money.cnn.com/2007/04/05/news/companies/ford_execpay/

23. Izuma, K., Saito, D.N., and Sadato, N., *Neuron*, 58 (2008), pp.284–294.

24. Kasser, Tim, and Sheldon, Kennon M., *Psychological Science*, 11 (2000), p.348.

25. Erk, Susanne, Spitzer, Manfred, Wunderlich, Arthur P., Galley, Lars, and Walter, Henrik, *NeuroReport*, 13 (2002), pp.2499–2503.

26. Keltner, D., et al., Stanford University Graduate School of Business Research Paper No. 1669, December 2000.

27. Gruenfeld, D.H., et al., *Journal of Personality and Social Psychology*, 95 (2008), pp.111–127.

28. *New York Times*, 10 April 2003; *DW-World* (Deutsche Welle English-language radio broadcast), 3 October 2002.

29. Lammers, Joris, and Stapel, Diederik A., *Journal of Personality and Social Psychology*, 97 (2009), pp.279–289.

30. *New York Times*, 13 January 2010.

31. http://www.time.com/time/covers/0,16641,19870406,00.html

32. Lammers, Joris, Stapel, Diederik A., and Galinsky, Adam D., *Psychological Science*, 21 (2010), p.737.

33. Fliessbach, K., et al., *Science*, 318 (2007), pp.1305–1308.
34. http://www1.uni-hamburg.de/rz3a035//police101.html
35. *New York Times*, Friday, 15 November 1991.
36. Morris, M.W., and Peng, K., *Journal of Personality and Social Psychology*, 67 (1994), pp.949–971.
37. Kusari, F., 'Predicting American Presidential Election Outcomes Based on Candidates' Power, Affiliation and Achievement Motives', PhD Dissertation, Graduate School of Applied and Professional Psychology, Rutgers University, New Jersey, 2010.
38. Winter, D.G., *Journal of Personality and Social Psychology*, 52 (1987), pp.196–202.
39. McClelland, D.C., *Power: The Inner Experience*, New York, Irvington Publishers, 1975, pp.66–67.
40. McClelland, David C., *Journal of Studies on Alcohol*, 38, pp.142–144.
41. Magee, J.C., and Langner, C.A., *Journal of Research in Personality*, 42 (2008), pp.1547–1559.
42. Schultheiss, O.C., et al., *Hormones and Behaviour*, 36 (1999), pp.234–241.
43. Chusmir, L.H., and Parker, B., *Sex Roles*, 11 (1984), pp.759–769.

6: *The Winning Mind*

1. Gottman, John, *The Mathematics of Marriage*, Cambridge, MA, MIT Press, 2003.
2. Cialdini, R.B., *The Psychology of Influence and Persuasion*, New York, Collins, 2007.
3. Magno E., Foxe, J.J., Molholm, S., Robertson, I.H., and Garavan, H., 'The anterior cingulate and error avoidance', *Journal of Neuroscience*, 26 (2006), pp.4769–4773.
4. Kochanska, G., et al., *Child Development*, 80 (2009), pp.1288–1300.
5. *New York Times*, 12 September 2007.
6. http://www.bbc.co.uk/pressoffice/pressreleases/stories/2005/10_october/06/bush.shtml
7. Rogow, A.A., and Lasswell, H.D., *Power, Corruption, and Rectitude*, Westport, CT, Greenwood Publishing Group, 1963.
8. Fast, N.J., and Chen, S., *Psychological Science*, 20 (2009), pp.1406–1413.
9. Peter, Laurence J., and Hull, Raymond, *The Peter Principle: Why Things Always Go Wrong*, New York, William Morrow and Company, 1969.
10. Weick, M., and Guinote, A., *Journal of Experimental Psychology*, 46 (2010), pp.595–604.

11. Robertson, Ian, *Mind Sculpture*, London, Bantam, 1999.
12. Smith, P.K., *Journal of Personality and Social Psychology*, 90 (2006), pp.578–596.
13. Kasser, T., *The High Price of Materialism*, Cambridge, MA, and London, MIT Press, 2002.
14. Lea, S.E.G., and Webley, P., *Behavioural and Brain Sciences*, 29 (2006), pp.161–209.
15. *New Scientist*, 7 May 2011, pp.10–11.
16. Nisbett, R.E., *The Geography of Thought*, New York, Free Press, 2005.

Afterword

1. Kipnis, David, in Lee-Chai, A.Y., and Bargh, J.A., *The Use and Abuse of Power*, New York, Taylor and Francis, 2001, pp.3–17.
2. Kasser, T., and Ryan, R.M., 'A dark side of the American dream: Correlates of financial success as a central life aspiration', *Journal of Personality and Social Psychology*, 65 (1993), pp.410–422.
3. Keshet, S., et al., *European Journal of Social Psychology*, 36 (2006), pp.105–117.
4. Winston, R., *Charlemagne: From the Hammer to the Cross*, London, Eyre and Spottiswoode, 1956, p.280; see also: http://www.britannica.com/EBchecked/topic/293922/Irene

Further Reading

Cialdini, R. B., *Influence: The Psychology of Persuasion* (New York: Collins, 2007)

Dweck, C. S., *Self-Theories: Their role in motivation, personality, and development* (Philadelphia, PA: The Psychology Press, 1999)

Gladwell, Malcolm, *Blink: The Power of Thinking Without Thinking* (New York: Little, Brown & Co., 2005)

Kasser, T., *The High Price of Materialism* (Cambridge, MA: The MIT Press, 2002)

Kipnis, D., *The Powerholders* (Chicago: University of Chicago Press, 1976)

Lee-Chai, A. Y., and J. A. Bargh, *The Use and Abuse of Power* (New York: Taylor & Francis, 2001)

Marmot, M., *Status Syndrome: How Social Standing Affects Our Health and Longevity* (London: Bloomsbury, 2004)

Nisbett, R. E., *The Geography of Thought* (New York: Free Press, 2005)

Robertson, Ian, *Mind Sculpture* (London: Bantam, 1999)

Russell, B., *Power: A New Social Analysis* (London: George Allen & Unwin, 1938)

Zimbardo, P., *The Lucifer Effect: How Good People Turn Evil* (London: Rider Books, 2007)

Index

Carter, Jimmy 227, 230, 246
Catherine the Great 280
CEO–prefrontal cortex analogy 115–16
certainty, and power 120
chameleon chemistry 68
chance 5, 55, 92–4
charitable donations 204–5
cheating 215
Cheney, Dick 113–14
Chernobyl nuclear power plant disaster 99–100, 101–3
chess 63
Chicago, University of 59
children
  helpless 38–9
  and power 256–9, 266
children of successful parents 9–15, 19–20, 26–7, 29–30
  underachievement 31–2
Chinese self, the 224–6
choking 200–2
Christianity 162–4, 168
Chrysler 181–2
Churchill, Winston 115, 279
Cialdini, Robert, *The Psychology of Influence and Persuasion* 241–2
circumstances 5, 55, 92–4, 274–5
Civil Rights Act (US) 88
Clare (typist) 149, 152–4, 159
clenched fist, the 76–7, 79–80
Clinton, Bill 6, 120, 246
  administration 103–4
  Blair's support for 95–6
  humiliations 97–8
  killer instinct 124–6
  Kosovo campaign, 1999 96–7, 98
  need for power 123–4, 134–5
  rift with Blair 98, 106, 112–13, 117, 133
  sense of control 112
  successes 98–9
Clinton, Hillary 82–3, 95
cocaine 196, 198
cognitive dissonance 141–2, 246–8, 250, 264
cojones summit, the 113–17
Cole, Steve 172
collective identity 274
collectivist perspective 221–6
Collins, Barry 159
colour, and performance 69–71
Columba of Iona, St 151
Columbia University 3, 40–1
  Teachers College 13–14
community, sense of 170
concentration camps 170, 176–7, 281
conditioned stimuli 177–9
conformity 219–20

Connecticut, University of 158–9
conscious bias 87
consistency 47–8, 247, 250
contempt 239, 249, 252–3, 271–2
context 270–1
control
  and bullying 250–6
  illusion of 110–12, 118–19
  loss of 153
  and money 205–6
  need for 175–6
  and power 256
  real winners and 275
  sense of 112–13, 154–60, 169
  and status 148–54
  and stress 148–52, 161–2
Cook, Robin 105
cookie study, the 207–8
Copenhagen, University of 12
corporate culture 224–5
corruption 262
cortisol 79, 124–6, 144–7, 172, 254
Covington, Martin 43
Crandall, Virginia 34, 40
criticism, lack of appreciation of 2
cruelty 7, 281
Cuban Missile Crisis 230–2
culture, and self 221–6

Dartmouth College 71
Darwin, Charles 172
DAT1 gene 192–3
D'Avanzo, Karen 13–14
Davis, Kristin 196
death 205–6
democracy 130, 267–9, 277, 282
deprivation 262
derivatives market 184
Dickerson, Sally 171–2, 173
dictators 198, 261–2, 282
Diener, Carol 34–9, 43
disappointments 188
discontent 28
Discovery of the Individual, 1050–1200, The (Morris) 163–4, 165
discrimination 81–2, 89
disempowerment 271
dominance relations 59–61, 61–4, 75–81
dominant-baboon effect 143–8
dopamine
  and compulsive gambling 186–90
  genetic influences 192–5
  Goldilocks zone 203
  and motivation 115
  and sex drive 192
  surge 119–20, 197,202

and testosterone levels 117
universally convertible currency 206
dorsal ACC (dACC) 245, 247–50, 251,
    252–3, 264
dorso-medial prefrontal cortex 167–8
DRD4 gene 193–4
Dreber, Anna 193–4
drinking 132, 230
drive to win 4
drugs and drug abuse 19–20, 65–7, 195–6,
    198, 279
Duckworth, Angela 47–8
Durham, University of 69–70
Dweck, Carol 34–9, 40, 42, 49–50, 141
Dyatlov, Anatoly 99–100, 101–2
Dyson, Stephen 112–13, 123

early childhood fatalism 271
economics, of success 13–14
Eden, James 2
education 267–8
ego 10–11, 51–2, 275, 278, 280
egocentricity 106–9, 207–19, 265
ego-goals 43
ego-vulnerability 43–5
Einstein, Albert 31
Einstein, Hans 31
Eisenhower, Dwight 115
Elizabeth I, Queen 151, 280
el-Mahroug, Karima 190–1
empathy, lack of 208
empowerment 267–9, 271
Enron 181–2, 195, 196–7, 199, 211, 213–14,
    216, 219, 220, 224–5, 235, 236, 280
entitlement 215, 216
entrepreneurs, succession 12
environment
    and body chemistry 66–7
    context 68–9
    dominance relations 59–61, 61–4
    financial traders 55–6
    and *Haplochromis burtoni* 53–5
    hierarchies 59–61
    home turf advantage 65, 71–5
    posture 75–81
    real winners and 274–5
    red 69–71
    and testosterone levels 55–7, 62–3
environmental cues 66–8
Ericsson, Anders 50–1
Erk, Susanne 206
Escobar, Andrées 57
esprit de corps 219–20
Eurozone crisis, 2011 132
evil 279
evolution 54

exceptionalism 216
Exeter, University of 269
exhaustion 259–60

Fast, Nathanael 110, 262
Fastow, Andrew 185, 219, 220, 224, 236
fatalism 49, 271
favours 241–2
fear 177–9
fear signals 178–9
feedback 35, 37, 81, 134
Feeney, Anne 81–2, 87
Fels Research Institute 34
Festinger, Leon 246–7
financial services 24–5
financial traders 55–6, 195, 212–13, 269
Firestone, Laurie 71–5
First Crusade 162
Fliessbach, Klaus 24–5, 217
Florida State University 50–1, 83, 163
fMRI (functional magnetic resonance imaging)
    22
Forbes 3
Ford 181–2, 201
Fortune 500, CEOs 11–12
Franklin, Ben 241–2, 250, 251
Free University, Amsterdam 76
freelance individuals 169
Frith, Christopher 200–1
functional magnetic resonance imaging (fMRI)
    22
Fuxjager, Matthew 64–5, 67–8, 73

Gaddafi, Muammar 198, 236–7, 283
Gaddafi, Saif 236–7
Gäfgen, Magnus 209–10
Galinsky, Adam 109
gambling 110, 185
    brain activity and 186–90
    compulsive 186–7
    DRD4 gene and 194
    pleasure of 189
    rewards 187–9
    and sex 192
Garavan, Hugh 196
Gates, Bill 27
gender, and power 132, 226–8, 234–5, 236,
    280
gender attitudes research 83–5
genes 46–7, 150–2
genetic fatalism 46–51
genetics 11–12
Genghis Khan 150, 151
genius 50–1
Getty, Balthazar 18–20
Getty, J. Paul, Snr 18, 18–19, 30–1, 32, 50

A NOTE ON THE AUTHOR

Ian Robertson is Professor of Psychology at Trinity College Dublin, Visiting Professor at University College London and Bangor University and is a Scientist at the Rotman Research Institute, University of Toronto. A trained clinical psychologist as well as a neuroscientist, he is widely known internationally for his work on attention and brain rehabilitation, is a member of the Royal Irish Academy and a Fellow of the Royal Society of Arts. His popular writing has included regular features in *The Times*, a column in the *British Medical Journal*, and many scientific books and articles. Ian has written three previous books aimed at the general reader: *Mind Sculpture* (2000), *The Mind's Eye* (2003) and *Stay Sharp* (2005), all of which have been widely translated. He is married with three children and lives in Dublin.